# ABOUT THIS BOOK

## SUBJECT MATTER

This book presents an introduction to English spelling. It is based on phonetic principles, and the grouping together of similar word forms and patterns.

It is also designed to help in the broadening of vocabulary and the understanding of the language, together with the development of writing and comprehension skills. A great deal of information has deliberately been included, in a precise but intelligible form.

Good spelling is not an optional extra to good English; it is an essential part of it. Its teaching should continue to form part of the English curriculum throughout every school, and up to school leaving age.

## LAYOUT

The format is that of a (re-usable) workbook. Each double page provides a factsheet on a particular topic facing a worksheet designed to test the understanding of the information and to help the child in its use. Putting the two together makes reference back very simple.

Each factsheet contains some background notes, together with a sample wordlist on the group or groups of words being taught. The worksheets consist of a set of exercises followed by spelling tests — lists of words for the child to learn for subsequent testing.

There is a page of revision exercises and a page of summary tests at the end of the book, together with an alphabetical wordlist and an index of main topics.

## USE

The factsheets may be used directly by the child as an information source. Alternatively they can provide the basis of the teaching content of a lesson, or as reinforcement for the teacher's own lesson plans and schemes of work.

The worksheets are intended to be used by children working alone or in groups, with support and assistance available from the teacher, or from parents.

This book can be readily used for work done at home.

A suggested marking scheme is provided for each exercise and the total for the exercises on each worksheet is fifty marks. Each test has ten questions, and there are five on a worksheet. Teachers may of course wish to vary the weightings given to individual exercises or to employ their own marking schemes.

However, it is envisaged that the marking of the exercises and tests *with* the children who have done them will in itself provide a useful teaching vehicle.

## AGE/ABILITY RANGE

The content of this book has been intensively tested with pupils as young as nine and as old as fifteen, with a remarkable degree of success.

More or less support will naturally be required from the teacher or parents depending on the age and ability of the children using the book.

The book is designed for top primary and lower secondary school pupils, or those in preparatory and middle schools, in the age range 9+ to 14+ and of average or above average ability. It can also be used as a revision primer for older pupils or as an aid for those learning English as a foreign language. The book would not generally be suitable for remedial teachings groups.

It is not essential to use the four other books in the *Help Yourself to English* series to be able to work from this book. However, the series as a whole, including the present title, does constitute a complete course in traditional English for the 9+ to 14+ age range.

The first part of this book deals with words that have a single sound. Each separate sound in a word is known as a 'syllable':—

*Bat* is a one-syllable word (because it has a single sound);
*Battle* has two syllables or sounds;
*Battlement* has three syllables.

Many short words are as hard to spell as longer ones. There are often two or more different ways of spelling words with exactly the same sound:—

*draft* (a rough plan) and *draught* (a cold wind)
*banned* (past tense of ban) and *band* (group of musicians *or* a circular strip).

All the one-syllable words here are arranged by SOUND, not by spelling. The reason for this is simple. We can all *say* these words already. We know what they sound like. What we cannot always do is *spell* them.

We begin with words that have an A-SOUND.

It may be a SHORT sound, as in *catch* or *jam*; or a LONG sound, as in *harm* and *charge*.

When it is a *long* A-sound, the A is often followed by the letter R.

For each group of words you will be given a WORDLIST, which will include most of the difficult words, as well as 'ordinary' spellings. Pairs of words with the same sound (correctly known as *homophones*) are put together. With each of them, and with any difficult words, you are frequently given a CLUE WORD, or a hint about the thing to watch out for. The clue often takes the form of the *meaning* of the word. With homophones you *must* learn the meaning with the spelling!

Here is the A-WORDS Wordlist:—

## WORDLIST

| | | | | | |
|---|---|---|---|---|---|
| catch | (ending always TCH) | jam | (a squash) | farce | (C) |
| | | jamb | (doorpost) | sparse | (S) |
| add | (double D) | lamb | (silent B) | | |
| | | | | heart | (blood) |
| laugh | (*Be careful!*) | banned | (from *ban*) | hart | (deer) |
| staff | | band | (group) | hearth | |
| draft | (rough plan) | | | | |
| draught | (cold wind) | chance | | carve | |
| | | France | | | |
| badge | | pants | | glass | (always SS) |
| flak | (gunfire) | ant | (insect) | gnash | (silent G) |
| plaque | (plate) | aunt | (relation) | chasm | (CH = C!) |
| quack | | | | spasm | |
| whack | (silent H) | can't | (cannot) | | |
| knack | (silent K) | shan't | (shall not) | passed | (from pass) |
| | | | | past | (former time) |
| packed | (from *pack*) | rap | (knock) | | |
| pact | (treaty) | wrap | (parcel) | gnat | (silent G) |
| tact | (politeness) | | | plait | (hair) |
| tacked | (from *tack*) | are | | maths | |
| | | bard | (poet) | | |
| pal | (one L) | barred | (with bars) | axe | |
| shall | | | | lacks | (from *lack*) |
| | | charge | | lax | (easy-going) |
| palm | | | | tacks | (from *tack*) |
| psalm | (hymn — P!) | arc | (circle) | | |
| qualm | (doubt) | ark | (Noah) | whacks | (from *whack*) |
| | | | | wax | (in candles) |
| calf | | bark | (tree) | | |
| calves | | barque | (ship) | ass | (donkey) |
| half | | clerk | (E *not* A!) | as | |
| halved | | | | | |
| | | gnarl | (silent G) | has | |
| dam | (barrier) | | | jazz | (double Z) |
| damn | (curse) | | | | |

Each Worksheet is divided into two sections — EXERCISES and SPELLING TESTS, as you can see on this page.

The exercises are intended to make you think about the spellings of the words, and to illustrate how they are used.

The tests check that you have really learnt the spelling — particularly the problem words and the homophones. You can of course make up other tests of your own, or mix up the words from different tests. Easy words (that are not necessarily included in the Wordlist on the opposite page) are also put in the tests — to make sure that you do not forget the 'normal' spellings.

## EXERCISES

(a) You should have noticed when you read through the Wordlist that several of the words have a SILENT LETTER. This of course means a letter which is there in the spelling but does not make any difference to the sound of the word.

Go through the Wordlist again, and make your own list of all those words which have one or more silent letters. Next to each word write the letters that are silent. (10)

(b) In each of the following examples you need to insert a pair of homophones (words with the same sound but different meanings). Write them out, putting the correct word in each space.

(1) The hunter shot the ............ through the ............ (hart, heart)

(2) That awful ............ has been ............ from the concert. (banned, band)

(3) My ............ are both terrified of ............ and spiders. (ants, aunts)*

(4) The hall was ............ with politicians, officials and people from the press and television, come to witness the signing of the ............ between the two countries. (pact, packed)

(5) Miss Pelling is far too ............ with her pupils: she ............ a proper sense of discipline. (lax, lacks) (10)

*Note: These words are not really homophones:— aunt has a long A, ant has a short A.

(c) In the following sentences you will find some strange spellings. Write out the sentences again, correcting the mistakes.

(1) "You will never cach me," cried the baron with an evil laff.

(2) Beneath the parm she sang a salm.

(3) He had an unpleasant nack of nashing his teeth.

(4) Mary had a little carf; she swapped it for her lam.

(5) On a trip to Franse he lost his pance. (20)

(d) This exercise is about some meanings that are not included in the Wordlist — so you may need a dictionary. For each meaning, write the correct spelling from the choice you are given.

(1) A spread or preserve usually made from fruit (jam, jamb)

(2) A circle, often of rubber or elastic, used for tying (banned, band)

(3) The sound made by a dog (bark, barque)

(4) A game played with round pieces on a board (drafts, draughts)

(5) Accuse someone of something (to tacks, to tax) (10)

## SPELLING TESTS

| 1 | 2 | 3 | 4 | 5 |
|---|---|---|---|---|
| apse | barge | plait | knack | laugh |
| snaps | gnat | draught | heart | staff |
| add | wax | draft | ask | gnash |
| guard | whacks | half | has | are |
| pal | as | halve | plaque | damn |
| shall | ass | psalm | rap | splash |
| aunt | clerk | farce | wrap | scratch |
| ant | thatch | badge | jazz | glance |
| branch | strap | starch | maths | harsh |
| shark | thank | scar | lamb | dam |

3

There is a second sound based on the letter A; what we might call the AI SOUND.

The trouble is that AI is not the only way it can be spelt.

Sometimes it is AI, as in:— *train, rail, maid,* — and the slightly different sound in *hair, pair.*

Sometimes it is A PLUS E: an A in the middle of the word, plus a silent E on the end, as in:— *sale, sane, ate, bare, save.* In fact this is probably the most common spelling. English often uses the SILENT E on the end of a word to change its sound.

Another spelling of the same sound is AY, as in:— *day, play, rays, stayed,* — and the similar *prayer.*

In addition there are other, more unusual spellings. The result is that there are very many HOMOPHONES with this sound. In fact the wordlist is largely made up of them. When you learn these words, remember to learn the 'clue word' along with the spelling.

## WORDLIST

| | | | | | |
|---|---|---|---|---|---|
| gray/grey | (the colour) | pail | (bucket) | knave | (rascal — K!) |
| | | pale | (white) | nave | (part of a church) |
| neigh | (horse sound) | | | | |
| | | sail | (boat) | wave | (watery bump) |
| pray | (say prayers) | sale | (selling) | waive | (give up a right) |
| prays | | | | | |
| prayer | | tail | (rear part) | baize | (green cloth) |
| praise | (worship) | tale | (story) | | |
| prey | (victim) | | | daze | (bewilder) |
| | | vale | (valley) | days | (from *day*) |
| slay | (to kill) | veil | (face-covering) | | |
| sleigh | (sledge) | | | maze | (puzzle) |
| | | wail | (weep) | maize | (corn) |
| they | | whale | (sea mammal) | | |
| | | Wales | (the country) | phrase | (part of sentence — PH!) |
| way | (route) | | | frays | (gets ragged) |
| weigh | (measure) | deign | (silent G) | | |
| whey | (curds & whey) | feign | (silent G)) | raise | (lift up) |
| weight | (heaviness) | | | rays | (sunbeams) |
| wait | (delay) | main | (chief) | raze | (destroy) |
| weighed | (from *weigh*) | mane | (lion's hair) | | |
| wade | (to paddle) | | | air | (atmosphere) |
| | | pain | (hurt) | heir | (inheritor — silent H) |
| laid | (from *lay*) | pane | (glass) | hair | (on your head) |
| lain | (from *lie*) | | | hare | (like a rabbit) |
| lane | (path) | plain | (flat/simple) | | |
| | | plane | (aeroplane) | bare | (naked) |
| made | (from *make*) | | | bear | (to suffer/the animal) |
| maid | (servant) | rain | (water) | | |
| | | rein | (bridle) | fair | (blond/carnival) |
| gauge | (AU not UA) | reign | (rule — GN!) | fare | (payment) |
| | | | | | |
| beige | (grey-brown) | skein | (bale *or* bundle) | mare | (horse) |
| | | | | mayor | (town leader) |
| ache | (pain — CH!) | vain | (proud) | | |
| | | vane | (wind indicator) | pair | (two) |
| brake | (stop) | vein | (blood vessel) | pear | (fruit) |
| break | (smash) | | | pare | (cut up small) |
| | | place | (location) | | |
| stake | (wood) | plaice | (fish) | stair | (steps) |
| steak | (meat) | | | stare | (look at) |
| | | waist | (your middle) | | |
| ail | (be ill) | waste | (use badly) | swear | (curse *or* promise) |
| ale | (beer) | | | | |
| | | ate | (from *eat*) | tear | (rip) |
| bale | (bundle) | eight | (the number) | | |
| bail | (payment) | | | there | (that place/there is) |
| | | gate | (door) | their/theirs | (of them) |
| gaol/jail | (prison) | gait | (way of walking) | they're | (they are) |
| | | | | | |
| hail | (snow/greet) | grate | (fireplace) | wear | (have clothes on) |
| hale | (healthy) | great | (large *or* mighty) | where | (which place) |
| | | | | wares | (goods for sale) |
| mail | (letters) | straight | (not bent) | | |
| male | (man) | strait | (narrow water) | | |
| | | | | | |
| | | wraith | (ghost — silent W!) | | |

4

# EXERCISES

a) You may have noticed in the Wordlist that for some words two meanings are given for the *same* spelling. The two meanings (or clue words) are separated by a slanting line (/). Make a list of all these words, and their alternative meanings.

There are also two cases where words of precisely the same sound and meaning have two different possible spellings listed. Note these words down also. (10)

b) Write out the following sentences, correcting all the spelling mistakes that you can find in them. Be sure to check with the Wordlist, or with your dictionary, as not all the words taken from the list have been spelt incorrectly!

   (1)   The mayor clambered onto his old grey mare.
   (2)   We have to pay our bus fair, and then the admission charge to the fare.
   (3)   The made made us a cup of tea.
   (4)   After his accident, he was in a days for daze.
   (5)   She laid the table, and then lay down on the sofa.
   (6)   Weight a minute, lad, and I'll show you the proper whey to way apples.
   (7)   In the grate a grate fire was blazing merrily.
   (8)   The male lion's mane distinguishing feature is his main.
   (9)   The building was raised to the ground by the aliens' death raise so that nothing remained to show where it had stood.
   (10)  A sinister vail of mist drifted across the dark vale beneath the towering walls of the castle of Belengar. (20)

c) You did an exercise of this type on the last Worksheet. Your job is to write out the sentences, inserting the correct homophone in each space.

   (1)   The blazing ............ made a safe landing on the flat ............ (plane, plain)
   (2)   It is unusual to see ............ in any large numbers around the coasts of ............ (wales, whales: in your answer do not forget to give the country its capital letter)
   (3)   Do you call this ............ a fish and chip shop, when there's no ............ on the menu? (plaice, place)
   (4)   The yacht slowly came round into the wind, and then made ............ for the narrow ............ between the jagged rocks. (strait, straight)
   (5)   If Jimmy heads that ball through my window-............, the ............ he'll feel will not be in his head. (pane, pain) (10)

d) This exercise is similar to the one you have just done. Once again your job is to write out the sentences, and insert the correct one of a pair of homophones into each space. There is a slight additional problem, however. This time you are not told what the pair of homophones is!

   (1)   The parade to mark the beginning of the king's ............ was spoilt by heavy showers of ............ throughout the day.
   (2)   We ............ our dinner, and hurried to get ready by ............ o'clock.
   (3)   I really must think of my ............-line; but on the other hand it would be a pity to ............ such an expensive cream cake.
   (4)   There was an ............ of excitement among the assembled servants, as the ............ to the estate and the dukedom finally came down the grand staircase to address his staff.
   (5)   The old man trudged with a stumbling, uncertain ............ up the long driveway, only to stop short as he found the ............ closed and barred against him. (10)

# SPELLING TESTS

| 1 | 2 | 3 | 4 | 5 |
|---|---|---|---|---|
| stain | way | trade | made | paid |
| strait | weigh | frays | maid | stayed |
| straight | plain | phrase | knave | glade |
| days | plane | tail | nave | plaice |
| daze | came | tale | rein | place |
| chase | claim | break | rain | praise |
| ace | gauge | brake | reign | prays |
| mayor | feign | neigh | square | heir |
| their | bear | whale | chair | air |
| there | bare | player | eight | wraith |

The next sound is the E-SOUND, and it does not present any great difficulties. The normal spelling is simply the letter E, as in:— *red, egg, pen, well, bench, fetch, deck.*

There are some alternative spellings though, and the main one is EA. You need to take care with EA words:—

Sometimes they have the same sound as AI, as in *steak* and *pear.*

Sometimes they have an EE sound, as in:— *sea* and *fear.*

On this Factsheet we are interested in the ones that have a simple SHORT E SOUND, such as:— *dead, head, deaf, health, threat, breath.*

We have already met homophones — words with the same sound but different spellings and meanings.

You also need to be careful about pairs of words which happen to have the same spelling, but have a completely different sound (and meaning):—

*Tear* (with one sound) is a drop of water in the eye; *tear* (with another sound) is a rip. Though I can *read* the paper today, I also *read* the paper yesterday. (Same spellings, but different sounds, to show the present and past tense).

One last thing to notice concerns the SILENT E on the end of words. As you know, this final E often changes the vowel sound in the middle of the word:— *Can* becomes *cane; pal* becomes *pale.*

Sometimes, however, the E is part of the (consonant) sound at the end of the word, as in:— *hedge* (not 'hej'), *twelve* (not 'twelv'), *else* (not 'els').

Try to remember little points like this, especially for words *you* find difficult.

## WORDLIST

| | | | | | |
|---|---|---|---|---|---|
| ebb | (double B) | dwell | (always double L) | when | (silent H) |
| web | | gel | (the exception!) | wren | (silent W) |
| fetch | (ending always TCH) | knell | (silent K) | wrench | (silent W) |
| bled | | quell | | friend | (I before E) |
| bread | (loaf) | sell | (for sale) | fence | |
| bred | (brought up) | cell | (prison room) | sense | |
| dread | | squelch | | whence | (silent H) |
| head | | whelk | (silent H) | scent | (perfume) |
| lead | (the metal) | elm | | sent | (from *send*) |
| led | (from *to lead*) | realm | | length | (GTH) |
| read | (from *to read*) | whelp | (silent H) | strength | (GTH) |
| red | (the colour) | else | | slept | |
| said | ("SED") | Welsh | | guess | (silent U) |
| says | ("SEZ") | Celt | | guessed | (from *guess*) |
| spread | | dealt | | guest | (visitor) |
| stead | | dwelt | | stress | (Always double S) |
| thread | | knelt | (silent K) | yes | (except in *yes*) |
| tread | | health | | flesh | |
| deaf | | stealth | | breast | |
| theft | | wealth | | rest | (peace/remainder) |
| egg | (double G) | twelfth | | wrest | (seize from) |
| hedge | | twelve | | debt | (silent B) |
| sledge | | gem | (G not J) | sweat | |
| check | (examine/square) | phlegm | ("FLEM"!) | threat | |
| cheque | (money order) | dreamt | (no P) | wet | (water) |
| wreck | (silent W) | tempt | (P) | whet | (sharpen) |
| sect | (religious group) | Thames | (silent H) | breath | |
| | | | | death | |

# EXERCISES

(a) Go through the Wordlist on the opposite page and make two lists:—

List (1) of words that have a silent W;

List (2) of words that have a silent H. (Note: Some people do pronounce the H in WH words!)     (10)

(b) Write out these sentences, and fill in the correct word in each space from the pair of homophones you are given:—

   (1)   I ............ the party to the shaft of the ............ mine. (lead, led)

   (2)   When you write a ............, always ............ the signature, date and amount. (cheque, check)

   (3)   I have heard of confidence tricksters, but Number 1996 has been trying to ............ his ............ to the governor. (cell, sell)

   (4)   I suppose I shall have to give her ............ for her birthday, even though I ............ perfume last year as well. (scent, sent)

   (5)   While the ............ of the knights looked on in horror, Sir Gawain sought to ............ the sword from Lancelot's hand. (wrest, rest)     (10)

(c) Go through the Wordlist very carefully, and make your own list of words that have a simple E SOUND, but are spelt with the letters EA. (The first one is *bread*.)     (10)

(d) In the following sentences you will find a few 'E words' spelt in rather an unusual way. Write out the sentences again, correcting the spelling mistakes.

   (1)   John sayed he would come, but he always sez that.

   (2)   I am quite sure I have red *The Decline and Fall of the Roman Empire*; it's a big read book isn't it?

   (3)   You hed him off wen he reaches the gully, Jake.

   (4)   Helth is more important that wealf.

   (5)   Joan was amazed to hear that the theaft of her priceless gems was carried out by one of her own guesseds.     (10)

(e) Write out the following sentences, putting in the word which has the correct spelling from the choice given you in the brackets.

   (1)   The farmer carefully paced out the (lenth, length, leanth) of the (fens, fense, fence).

   (2)   Jackie would never have (drempt, dreamt, dremt) that her closest (freind, friend, fiend) Felicity would stoop so low as to put oil in her hockey boots.

   (3)   "This requires great skill," said William as he (nelt, knealt, knelt) down on the floor beside the radio. "Just hand me that monkey (wrench, rench, wreanch), will you?"

   (4)   "I was born and (bread, brede, bred) beside the river," said old George, "and there isn't an inch of the (Tames, Thames, Tems) I don't know."

   (5)   "Behold the (reck, wreak, wreck) of your Round Table, Arthur," cried Mordred. "Soon nothing will remain of all your vaunted (relm, realme, realm)."     (10)

# SPELLING TESTS

| 1 | 2 | 3 | 4 | 5 |
|---|---|---|---|---|
| theft | health | edge | else | read (*present tense*) |
| lead (*metal*) | debt | fence | quench | read (*past tense*) |
| led | Thames | dense | crept | red |
| friend | thread | meant | stepped | wreck |
| ebb | guest | deaf | tread | says |
| web | guessed | said | cell | dreamt |
| squelch | wretch | knelt | sell | tempt |
| death | length | dealt | check | scent |
| twelve | phlegm | strength | cheque | sent |
| wrench | gem | threat | sweat | wren |

If you find the spelling tests a little too easy (as you may at this stage), try doing them when you are only given the *meaning* of the word, not the actual word at all. If you have learnt the words thoroughly first, you should still be able to do the tests.

You know very well the sound made by putting EE or EA together: it is one of the first you learn when you start to read.

As well as the EE and EA spellings, there are also several words that have a SILENT E on the end (such as: *these, mere, scene*); and rather more words that are spelt IE (such as *thief, field, pier*). Notice that it is normally IE not EI (except in *seize, weir, weird,* — and some longer words when EI follows the letter C).

Because of all these alternative spellings (plus some even odder variations), there are very many homophones for this sound once again. Most of them are included in the Wordlist, together with 'problem' words; but there are of course many other 'simple' words that have been left out.

## WORDLIST

| | | | | | |
|---|---|---|---|---|---|
| be | (to be) | weal | (mark of blow) | cease | (to stop) |
| bee | (insect) | wheel | (round thing) | crease | |
| | | we'll | (we shall) | grease | |
| flea | (insect) | field | | lease | |
| flee | (run away) | shield | | | |
| | | wield | | peace | (quiet) |
| key | (unlocks) | yield | | piece | (part) |
| quay | (harbour) | | | | |
| | | scheme | (CH not K) | niche | (recess) |
| knee | (silent K) | | | | |
| | | seam | (join in cloth) | priest | |
| sea | (ocean) | seem | (appear to be) | | |
| see | (look at) | | | beat | (punish/defeat) |
| | | team | (players) | beet | (sugar beet) |
| tea | (drink) | teem | (be full of) | | |
| tee | (in golf) | | | feat | (achievement) |
| | | theme | | feet | (on the legs) |
| need | (want *or* lack) | | | | |
| knead | (make dough) | bean | (vegetable) | meat | (food) |
| | | been | (from *to be*) | meet | (right and proper) |
| read | (book) | | | mete | (deal out) |
| reed | (plant) | scene | (setting) | | |
| | | seen | (from *to see*) | wheat | (silent H) |
| brief | (short) | | | | |
| chief | | cheap | (not dear) | wreath | (flower circle) |
| grief | (sorrow) | cheep | (birdsong) | wreathe | (to encircle) |
| thief | | | | sheath | |
| | | beer | (ale) | sheathe | |
| league | (GUE) | bier | (coffin rest) | | |
| | | | | eave | (roof edge) |
| siege | | dear | (valuable) | eve | (evening) |
| | | deer | (animal) | | |
| creak | (squeak) | | | grieve | (be sorrowful) |
| creek | (stream) | hear | (listen) | thieve | (to steal) |
| | | here | (this place) | | |
| leak | (water) | | | heave | |
| leek | (vegetable) | mere | | leave | |
| | | | | | |
| peak | (mountain) | peer | (lord/gaze) | peeve | (annoy) |
| peek | (sly look) | pier | (jetty) | sleeve | |
| pique | (sulk) | | | | |
| | | sear | (scorch) | weave | (cloth) |
| shriek | (scream) | seer | (prophet) | we've | (we have) |
| | | | | | |
| weak | (not strong) | sphere | (PH) | freeze | (cold) |
| week | (seven days) | | | frieze | (border) |
| | | tear | (crying) | | |
| heal | (make better) | tier | (level *or* rank) | ease | |
| heel | (foot) | | | please | |
| he'll | (he will) | weir | (river barrier) | tease | |
| | | weird | (strange) | | |
| kneel | (silent K) | | | cheese | |
| | | fierce | | | |
| peal | (bells) | pierce | | seize | (take) |
| peel | (skin) | | | | |
| | | niece | | these | |
| real | (true) | | | | |
| reel | (cotton/dance) | fleece | (wool) | breeze | |
| | | geese | (goose) | sneeze | |
| steal | (rob) | | | wheeze | |
| steel | (metal) | | | | |

## EXERCISES

a) Write out the following sentences, putting the correct word, from the pairs of homophones you are given, in each space.

    (1)    If you come over ............ and listen, you can ............ the mice moving about behind the skirting board. (here, hear)

    (2)    On the ............, braving the sea breezes, stood a ............ of the realm, in full regalia. (peer, pier)

    (3)    The books which the ancient Egyptians used to ............ were scrolls made from the papyrus ............ . (read, reed)

    (4)    Josiah had ............ quietly raking over his ............ patch, when, quite by chance, he had ............ that remarkable ............ (been, bean / scene, seen)        (10)

b) Not all the words with the EE/EA sound are included in the Wordlist. Here are five more EE/EA words. Look up each in your dictionary, and write its meaning next to it. (You might also notice that they all have curious spellings.)

    (1) fief        (2) liege        (3) clique        (4) wreak        (5) mien        (10)

c) This is another exercise on words *not* in the list, but which you should know. Your job is to choose the correct spelling from the alternatives given you in the brackets. (You may well find that you need your dictionary again.)

    (1)    "I don't know what you (meen, mene, mean), inspector," said the butler. "I have never seen him before in my life."

    (2)    "Oh dear, I shall need a new reel of (grene, grean, green) cotton to mend this tear," muttered Steve's mother. "He really is so careless."

    (3)    "Try to steer a little more to the right, Mr Fortinbras," (screeched, scrieched, screached) the driving instructor. "That's the third wing-mirror we've collected from those parked cars."

    (4)    Through the lattice (screan, screne, screen) I could just see the three men around the table.

    (5)    Eve did not find the apple (sweet, sweat, swete) enough for her taste.        (10)

(d) In the above sentences, there are ten one-syllable (i.e. single sound) words that have the EE/EA sound — though not necessarily the EE/EA spelling. These are in addition to the words in brackets. Make a list of the extra ten words.        (10)

(e) Insert the correct spelling in each space from the choices you are given:—

    (1)    It is very ............, right and our bounden duty that we should at all times and in all places give thanks unto Thee. (mete, meat, meet)

    (2)    We ............ for the loss of our dear friend. (grief, grieve, greive)

    (3)    He intended to ............ the boy who had been stealing his sugar. (beat, beet, bete)

    (4)    There ............ to be some poor stitching along this join. (seams, seems, seemes)

    (5)    Jason gave a quick look at the snow-crowned ............ above him, gulped and returned to his sulks. (pique, peak, peek)        (10)

## SPELLING TESTS

| 1 | 2 | 3 | 4 | 5 |
|---|---|---|---|---|
| each | speed | dream | wreath | freeze |
| she | bead | eel | wreathe | frieze |
| siege | scheme | kneel | grief | theme |
| key | knead | cheese | weak | feet |
| quay | need | mean | week | feat |
| thief | niece | weird | niche | sphere |
| piece | weave | fierce | seize | priest |
| peace | pier | wheat | seas | tear |
| scene | peer | weal | sneeze | tier |
| seen | shield | wheel | ease | league |

There is nothing difficult about words with an I-SOUND:— *lid, cliff, stitch, grin, till.*

You sometimes find a SILENT E on the end, but only when it is part of the consonant sound at the end of the word, as in words that end in IDGE, INGE, INCE and INSE:— *bridge, fringe, prince, rinse* for example.

Be careful with *give* and *live*. The E is part of the V sound; there are no English words that end in V by itself.

But *live* has two pronunciations and two meanings: *live* to rhyme with *give* (meaning 'to be alive'); and *live* to rhyme with *dive* (meaning 'not dead').

There are many other words with I in the middle and a silent E on the end: but they of course have a different sound (as in *time, strike* and *kite*) and they are dealt with on the next Factsheet.

There are several I-WORDS that have silent letters, and you have already met them in other words we have looked at. So it is worth mentioning some of the examples:—

There is a SILENT B on the end of *limb*. This MB ending turns up on several words. We have seen it on *lamb*, and it will re-appear on *tomb* and *climb*, — and others.

*Wrist* and *wring* start with a SILENT W. We have already come across *wrap* and *wren*; — *write* and *wrong* (among others) will come later.

There is a SILENT K on *knit* — much as there was on *knack, knell* and *kneel*; and you have also encountered a SILENT G (*gnarl* and *gnat*) — though no I-WORD has one.

The H which follows the W in many English words (*which, what, when* etc.) tends to be a silent letter now, though it used to be pronounced quite clearly.

One last note on I-WORDS: the letter I by itself can spell the rather different IE sound which comes on the next Factsheet. Be careful with words like *wind* (gale) and *wind* (turn a handle).

## WORDLIST

| | | | | | |
|---|---|---|---|---|---|
| squib | | him | (he) | whip | (silent H) |
| squid | | hymn | (sacred song — MN!) | crypt | (Y not I) |
| ditch | (usual ending TCH) | limb | (silent B) | miss | (usually SS) |
| rich | (CH) | whim | (wish) | this | (except *this*) |
| which | (that *or* what) | lymph | (Y not I/PH not F) | disc/disk | (flat circle) |
| witch | (magician) | glimpse | | whisk | (silent H) |
| midst | | in | (into) | chrism | (the CH is like K) |
| cliff | (usually FF) | inn | (tavern) | prism | |
| if | (except *if*) | gin | | schism | ('sism') |
| thrift | | inch | | cyst | (swelling) |
| bridge | | wind | (gale) | tryst | (meeting) |
| stick | | ring | (circle) | missed | (from *to miss*) |
| strict | | wring | (to twist) | mist | (fog) |
| kill | (usually LL) | fringe | | whist | (card game) |
| nil | (except *nil*) | ink | (always K) | wrist | (silent W) |
| build | (silent U) | zinc | (except *zinc*) | knit | (wool) |
| built | | mince | (CE) | nit | (lice) |
| gild | (coat with gold) | rinse | (SE) | whit | ('not a whit') |
| guild | (trade association) | plinth | | wit | (humour/sense) |
| gilt | (gold-coated) | jinx | (bad luck) | writ | (a document) |
| guilt | (responsibility) | jinks | (as in 'high jinks') | give | |
| filth | | minx | | live | (the verb *to live*) |
| grim | | sphinx | (PH) | sieve | |
| gym | (Y!) | | | | |

## EXERCISES

(a) The first exercise is to do some research.
Go through the first five Wordlists, and make your own lists of all the words that have the following silent letters in them:— B, G, H, K, W. Do a separate list for each letter. Count the H in WH as silent.
Then, for the sake of your own spelling, make a particular effort to learn them! (10)

(b) In the following six sentences, there are ten errors in spelling, all involving words in the Wordlist.
Write out the sentences, correcting the spellings and underlining the words you have put right.

   (1)   Thriffed is an important virtue.

   (2)   Wich which made the grime prediction of her death?

   (3)   Our teacher is very stricked.

   (4)   Please mis, what does 'sism' mean?

   (5)   Though I rinced it in cold water, the inc would not come out.

   (6)   Cross your briges when you come to them. (10)

(c) Write out the following sentences, choosing the correct homophone from the pair given in the brackets.

   (1)   The candle sticks were silver- (guilt, gilt).

   (2)   I thought I told you never to (wring, ring) me at work.

   (3)   There is a meeting of the (Gild, Guild) of Goldsmiths today.

   (4)   Unfortunately we (missed, mist) each other in the (missed, mist).

   (5)   Mr Tenor was trying to teach (him, hymn) a new (hymn, him). (10)

(d) There are very many simple I-SOUND words not included in the list. In this exercise you are provided with the *meaning* or *definition* of a few of them. Your job is to find the word! Write out the definition with the word in your answers.

   (1)   ............ a sharp throbbing pain (often caused by insects or nettles)

   (2)   ............ to play a game of jumping over a rope

   (3)   ............ a faint shade or suggestion of colour

   (4)   ............ to turn (yourself or an object) round, usually several times

   (5)   ............ made a drawn out sound like an S (Be careful: you need the *past* tense!)

         Award yourself a bonus if you can get TWO answers for number three. (10)

(e) This is another exercise where you have to choose the correct spelling from several alternatives. The words are NOT in the Wordlist, so use your dictionary if you are not sure.

   (1)   We carefully climbed the (rije, rige, ridge) towards the distant summit.

   (2)   The door swung silently open on its (hinjes, hinges, hinjs).

   (3)   It hurt so much that he (winst, winsed, winced) at every step.

   (4)   She spent the entire afternoon dropping (hince, hinse, hints) about her birthday.

   (5)   We have all (sined, sind, sinned) in thought, word and deed. (10)

## SPELLING TESTS

| 1 | 2 | 3 | 4 | 5 |
|---|---|---|---|---|
| sing | whip | prince | quill | switch |
| singe | rich | whisk | nil | squid |
| which | stitch | wish | crypt | hymn |
| witch | quilt | stick | midst | him |
| build | inn | strict | thrift | glimpse |
| filled | in | guilt | limb | wrist |
| kiss | with | lymph | sphinx | squint |
| zinc | smith | rinse | ring | plinth |
| give | gin | live | wring | writ |
| sieve | prism | chrism | gym | schism |

This particular sound, which we have called the IE/Y sound is, as you would hope, sometimes spelt IE or Y, as in:— *tie, die, fly, sky.*

Be careful when you are changing the ending of a Y-word:— *fly : flies, try : tried* etc. You have to *change the Y to I,* and then add *ES or ED.*

The most common spelling of IE/Y words, however, is with the SILENT E on the end. The SILENT E makes the I in the middle of the word *long* instead of short, as in:— *pin — pine; strip — stripe; slim — slime.* You should not of course have any difficulty with this sort of word.

You do need to watch out for words that end in IGH and IGHT though. For some reason the letter I seems to attract these awkward endings, as in:— *high, night, right, sight.*

Finally, there are some words, ending in IND or ILD which have the IE SOUND, but for some reason do not need an E on the end of the word, such as: *find, kind, wild, child.*

In all of these groups of words, try to concentrate on those which you find particularly difficult. You will know most of them automatically already, but where there is some particular sound, or spelling variation, that gives you trouble, it is worth making your own notes of the problem words, and keeping a special list of your own.

## WORDLIST

| | | | | | |
|---|---|---|---|---|---|
| buy | (purchase) | rhyme | (verse) | blight | (GHT) |
| by | (beside) | rime | (frost) | bright | (GHT) |
| die | (death) | thyme | (silent H: herb) | fight | (GHT) |
| dye | (change colour) | time | (o'clock) | flight | (GHT) |
| died | (dead) | Rhine | (the river) | fright | (GHT) |
| dyed | (coloured) | sign | (a notice) | light | (GHT) |
| eye | (for seeing) | sine | (in maths) | plight | (GHT) |
| I | (me) | | | slight | (GHT) |
| aye | (yes) | whine | (squeal) | tight | (GHT) |
| high | (GH) | wine | (drink) | kite | (ITE) |
| nigh | (GH; near) | wind | (*to wind* a clock) | quite | (ITE) |
| rye | (corn) | bind | | spite | (ITE) |
| wry | (twisted) | blind | | sprite | (ITE) |
| sigh | (GH) | find | | trite | (ITE) |
| thigh | (GH) | grind | | height | (Notice EI) |
| why | | kind | | might | (power/maybe) |
| guide | (silent U) | mind | | mite | (insect/small sum) |
| side | (edge/surface) | type | (print/category) | night | (not day) |
| sighed | (from *to sigh*) | buyer | | knight | (in armour) |
| tide | (sea) | choir | (singers) | right | (correct/not left) |
| tied | (fastened) | quire | (sheets of paper) | rite | (religious service) |
| knife | (silent K) | dire | (serious) | write | (with a pen) |
| dike/dyke | (sea barrier) | dyer | (from *dye*) | wright | (craftsman) |
| aisle | (church) | friar | (monk) | sight | (vision) |
| isle | (island) | frier/fryer | (from *fry*) | site | (location) |
| I'll | (I shall) | higher | (from *high*) | cite | (mention *or* quote) |
| guile | (deceit) | hire | (rent or wage) | white | (the colour) |
| stile | (fence crossing) | liar | (tells lies) | Wight | (the Island) |
| style | (way of writing) | lyre | (instrument) | blithe | (happy) |
| while | (short time) | prior | (earlier/senior monk) | scythe | (sickle) |
| wild | (fierce) | pyre | (funeral fire) | writhe | (squirm) |
| wiles | (cunning) | tire | (grow tired) | live | (adjective, = alive) |
| child | | tyre | (on a wheel) | guise | (false appearance) |
| mild | | ice | (CE not SE) | prize | |
| climb | (go up) | Christ | | iron | (!) |
| clime | (climate) | bite | (teeth) | | |
| | | bight | (a bay or gulf) | | |
| | | byte | (in computing) | | |

*Note:* We have included IRE words on this page, even though they really have two sounds or syllables.

## EXERCISES

(a) In the Wordlist there were a couple of words with a SILENT U. Make a list of all the words you can find in the first six Wordlists that have a silent U. (Do not forget to include the ones in the Wordlist opposite.)   (10)

(b) Make a list of all the different ways you can find of spelling the IRE sound (as in *fire* for example). For each alternative spelling, give up to three examples — if you can. Some spellings may only happen in one or two words.
Your list should start something like this:—
IRE     examples: *fire, spire, wire*   (10)

(c) (1)   Give the past tense of the following words.
(For example: *talk — talked; speak — spoke.*)
die          dye          sigh          tie          fly
(2)   Give the plural of the following words.
(For example: *girl — girls; knife — knives.*)
cry          sky          tie          sigh          buy
(Watch out for tricks in this little exercise . . . )   (10)

(d) This is quite a tricky exercise too. Your job is to insert in each of the two spaces in the sentences a pair of homophones. Of course, if you were given the pair of homophones at the end of every sentence it would not be tricky at all. That is the reason you are not given the homophones. You have to select the ones that fit from the Wordlist.
Here is an example: "I have the power and ............ to crush you beneath my heel like the insignificant ............ you are." The words that belong in the spaces are *might* (= strength) and *mite* (tiny creature) — in that order.
(1)   Sir Guzzelot, the Black ............ rode steadily on through the dark ............ .
(2)   Rounding the headland, we saw before us the ............ cliffs of the Isle of ............ rising out of the sea.
(3)   When the sauce has cooled sufficiently, it is ............ to sprinkle it with some parsley or ............ as a final garnish.
(4)   The charges for the ............ of household appliances seem to get ............ every day.
(5)   I shall require from you ............ of papers you intend to ............ in this case, Miss Bunberry.   (10)

(e) Re-write this short passage from a ghost story, correcting the spelling mistakes:—
Wile the whiled wind wined down the chimney, Florence tried to fite off the sense of apprehension which had siezed her. The lihgt of the candles flickered suddenly in a sligth breeze, and the flames of the fier seemed to dye away. From outside the window, in a sudden lull in the howling of the gale, came a faint but haunting sighe.   (10)

## SPELLING TESTS

| 1 | 2 | 3 | 4 | 5 |
|---|---|---|---|---|
| spice | die | dry | sky | quite |
| by | dye | eye | high | guide |
| buy | child | rhyme | wry | ride |
| climb | filed | while | aisle | tied |
| thigh | knife | flier | isle | sighed |
| type | ice | dyer | sign | style |
| choir | wind (verb) | buyer | scythe | tire |
| site | fight | higher | knight | tyre |
| sight | liar | spire | wise | spite |
| writhe | prior | slight | prize | height |

As with A, E and I, the letter O by itself makes its own straightforward O-SOUND, as in: *frog, off, rock, cloth, pond.*

You need to be slightly careful, because O by itself sometimes makes a different, LONG O sound — as in *ghost, roll, fold, both, comb* — all of which you will find on the next Factsheet!

There are some O words which have a silent E on the end, as part of the consonant sound at the end, such as *dodge, lodge, bronze.* You have seen this sort of spelling plenty of times before, in words like *badge, edge* and *ridge.*

Perhaps the most difficult group of words that have an O-SOUND, but certainly not an O-SPELLING are these:—

| | | | | | | |
|---|---|---|---|---|---|---|
| watch | quad | quaff | waft | wan (which means pale and sickly) | | swamp |
| wand | wash | squash | quash | want | squat | was | wad |
| wasp | wrath | swat | swap | what | watt | swab | swan |

You will already know the common words in this list, but the other ones with an O-SOUND but an A-SPELLING need to be learnt carefully.

Of course these are not the oddest of such words. There is also *John,* the most mis-spelt name, and *yacht* (one of the strangest spellings in the English language).

Really, though, the O-sound is not particularly difficult. However, O does combine with various other letters, to make a whole series of other sounds, which you will meet on some of the following Factsheets.

## WORDLIST

| | | | |
|---|---|---|---|
| knob | (silent K) | bloc | (group of countries) |
| swab | (sponge or pad) | block | (obstruct/solid piece) |
| loch | (Scottish lake) | knock | (silent K) |
| lough | (Irish lake) | wok | (frying pan; *no* C) |
| (For both these words try saying '*lokh*') | | doll | (double L) |
| Scotch | (TCH) | col | (a ridge; *one* L) |
| Scots | | golf | |
| watch | | solve | |
| rod | (usually one D) | bomb | (silent B) |
| odd | (but *odd* is odd) | romp | |
| wad | (bundle) | swamp | |
| cough | (OU & GH) | prompt | (P) |
| off | (away) | don | (to put on) |
| of | (belongs to) | gone | |
| quaff | (to drink) | John | (silent H) |
| trough | (OU & GH) | swan | |
| oft | (= often) | wan | |
| waft | (blow) | wand | |
| log | | pond | |
| lodge | | wrong | (silent W) |
| quad | (courtyard) | font | |
| | | want | |

| | |
|---|---|
| bronze | |
| swap/swop | (exchange) |
| cross | (always double S) |
| quash | (reject) |
| squash | (flatten/a drink) |
| wash | |
| wasp | |
| not | (no) |
| knot | (tie) |
| squat | |
| swat | |
| what | (which) |
| watt | (electricity) |
| yacht | |
| wrath | (anger — noun) |
| wroth | (angry — adjective) |
| cloth | |
| ox | |
| box | |
| clocks | |
| socks | |
| was | |

The Wordlists given on these pages are of course general lists, designed to cover all the difficult spellings in a particular group of words. You will have your own particular problem words (everyone does), and it is sensible to keep a notebook in which you make your own wordlist, which only contains those words *you* have trouble spelling.

## EXERCISES

(a)  In the Wordlist opposite you will find some words that end in GH. Go through all of the first seven Wordlists, and make a list of all the words you can find ending in GH. (Do not include words ending in GHT.)    (10)

(b)  Write down four words that RHYME with each of the following words. You are not allowed to use words that are on the Wordlist.

(For example, if you were given *'cross'*, you could write *loss, moss, toss, boss*)

squat          box          wrong          swamp          wrath          (20)

(c)  In the following passage, obviously from a very sad story, some of the words have been given alternative spellings. Write out the passage, inserting the correct spelling from the alternatives you are given.

She seized the door-(knob, nob, nobb) and tried to turn it, but to no avail. The door was (lockt, locked, loked) and barred against her. A volley of despairing (knocks, nocks, nox) on the unyielding wood produced no response from those within. Hopelessly she pressed her pale, (won, wan, whon) face to the window. A (not, knot, knott) of people clustered round the blazing fire. She could hear their noisy chatter (woft, waffed, waft) through the cold night air. She (coffed, cought, coughed) weakly in the bitter chill. One of the guests chanced to look up towards the window.

"(Wat, What, Watt) is that?" he exclaimed. "There is a face at the window. You there, what do you (wont, wand, want)?" Before he had finished speaking, the face was (gorn, gon, gone).    (10)

(d)  Insert the correct homophone in the gaps in the following sentences. There are not many homophones among the O-WORDS, so you are not given the words, but each sentence contains a pair of homophones that can be found in the Wordlist.

(1)  The countries of the Eastern ............ combined to ............ any progress in the talks.

(2)  ............ Ness in Scotland is the longest lake in the British Isles, but ............ Neagh in Ireland is the largest.

(3)  If the ............ is a unit of electricity, ............ is the ohm?

(4)  No, you silly boy, that is ............ the way to tie a ............ in your tie.

(5)  Great was the ............ of Form 2B at the French teacher for the wrong they had suffered at her hands, and ............ words did they speak against her.    (10)

## SPELLING TESTS

| 1 | 2 | 3 | 4 | 5 |
|---|---|---|---|---|
| frog | off | flock | shop | shod |
| crock | of | doll | cost | fond |
| solve | ox | loss | throng | golf |
| prompt | cloth | lodge | rock | moth |
| swamp | knock | knob | quad | wasp |
| waft | wad | swan | wand | watch |
| wrath | bomb | want | squat | knot |
| bronze | gone | font | Scotch | yacht |
| odd | wash | trough | cough | was |
| squash | what | scoff | quaff | wrong |

We are calling this sound OE (as in *toe, woe, goes; hoe, hoes* and *hoed*), but that is not in fact its most common spelling.

It is often spelt OW, as in *blow* and *blown; throw* and *thrown; grow, grown* and *growth*. You must be careful with OW though; it spells a different sound in words like *now* and *town!*

Another spelling of the OE sound is in fact OA, as in *coach, road, oak, soap, coast.*

The most common spelling, though, is O plus a SILENT E on the end of the word:— *robe, code, home, bone, note, owe* — and many others.

In words where O is followed by L, the sound is very similar to the OE sound we are talking about now, and the spellings are often much the same (such as *pole, coal, bowl*). But there are some spellings where you might expect an E in the end and there isn't one (like *cold, gold* and *colt*), and there are some words with the mysterious silent U that we have met with before (like *soul, mould* and *moult*).

Of course all these alternative spellings mean that there are many homophones about, and they are the things you need to be particularly careful with.

## WORDLIST

| | | | | | |
|---|---|---|---|---|---|
| bow | (for arrows/knot) | toad | (frog) | loan | (lend) |
| doe | (female deer) | towed | (from *tow*) | lone | (alone) |
| dough | (pastry) | loaf | | moan | (groan) |
| foe | (enemy) | rogue | (GUE ending) | mown | (from *mow*) |
| hoe | (for gardening) | cloak | | phone | |
| fro | ('to and fro') | croak | | shown/shewn | (from *show*) |
| go | | oak | | throne | (chair) |
| goes | | soak | | thrown | (from *throw*) |
| no | (not) | folk | (silent L) | gross | (144/very large) |
| know | (understand) | yolk | (silent L) | ghost | (silent H) |
| nose | | bowl | (dish/to throw) | host | |
| owe | (debt) | bole | (tree trunk) | most | |
| row | (with oars/a line) | coal | | post | |
| roe | (fish eggs) | foal | | roast | |
| show/shew | (point out) | goal | | toast | |
| so | (therefore) | shoal | | bloat | |
| sow | (seeds) | hole | (pit) | boat | |
| sew | (stitch) | whole | (all) | coat | |
| though | (OUGH) | role | (part in a play) | gloat | |
| throw | (let fly) | roll | (turn over) | goat | |
| throe | (a fit) | sole | (foot/only/fish) | stoat | |
| tow | (pull) | soul | (spirit) | throat | |
| toe | (on your foot) | mould | (OU) | moat | (water) |
| woe | (grief) | moult | (OU) | mote | (speck) |
| whoa | (said to horses) | bolt | (lock/run off/ | wrote | (from *write*) |
| broach | (to open) | | bundle of cloth) | rote | (by heart) |
| brooch | (jewellery) | comb | (silent B) | oath | |
| coach | | chrome | (CH) | both | |
| poach | | foam | | growth | |
| goad | | loam | | clothe | (*to clothe*, verb) |
| woad | | roam | (wander) | loth/loath | (unwilling) |
| load | (on a lorry) | Rome | (the city) | loathe | (to detest) |
| lode | (vein of gold) | blown | | mauve | (purple) |
| ode | (poem) | known | | coax | |
| owed | (debt) | own | | hoax | |
| road | (route) | groan | (moan) | close | (to shut — Z sound) |
| rode | (from *ride*) | grown | (increased) | close | (near — S sound) |
| rowed | (from *row*) | | | froze | |
| | | | | those | |

## EXERCISES

(a)  In this pleasant little story you will find ten words, all with an OE sound, that have been spelt incorrectly. Write out the story again, putting the spellings right. Underline the word that you have corrected.

>     The ship rocked to and froe, as the sea gently rows and fell. A loan and silent sailor stood at the wheel. The creak and grown of the weary timbers and the gentle slap of the fome on the ancient oke were the only sounds to break the unending quiet. A cloke of mist clowthed the ocean in its clammy shroud. There would not ever be a wind to blough that ship to land, and the hand that clasped the wheel had fingers made of brittle bown.     (10)

(b)  Each of the following requires a pair of homophones to be inserted in the gaps. You are not given the words, so you need to search through the Wordlist until you find a suitable pair that will make sense; then you need to make sure you put the right one in the right place!

    (1)  As I fell into the gaping ............ my ............ life flashed before my eyes.

    (2)  When dad had ............ the grass, he collapsed into the deck-chair with a low ............ of exhaustion.

    (3)  In the test we ............ down the spellings we had learnt by ............ the day before.

    (4)  There would be ............ excuse if we did not ............ the answers.

    (5)  "Oh, Clarence, what a simply adorable diamond ............ you have given me for my birthday!"
        "Oh, Ermintrude, I'm so glad you like it. Shall we ............ a bottle of bubbly to celebrate the occasion?"     (10)

(c)  Write a sentence of your own explaining the meaning of each of the following words. As you will see, the words are all in groups of homophones.
(For example:— HOLE: "A hole is a pit or opening dug into the ground or through some other material." Notice that you are asked to give the meaning, not 'to use the word in a sentence'.)

| (1) moat | (2) tow | (3) road | (4) so |
|----------|---------|----------|--------|
| mote | toe | rode | sow |
|  |  | rowed | sew |

    (10)

(d)  In this exercise your job is to give some examples, from the Wordlist or from your own knowledge of the different ways in which the OE SOUND is spelt.

    (1)  Give four words where the OE SOUND is spelt OU.

    (2)  Give six words where the OE sound is spelt O, plus a SILENT E on the end.

    (3)  Give six words where the OE sound is spelt OW.

    (4)  Give four words where the OE sound is spelt simply with a letter O.

    (5)  Give six words where the OE sound is spelt OA.

    (6)  Finally, give four words where the OE sound is spelt — OE.     (20)

## SPELLING TESTS

| 1 | 2 | 3 | 4 | 5 |
|---|---|---|---|---|
| bow | chrome | dough | though | rode |
| go | owe | brooch | rogue | rowed |
| hoe | woe | poach | comb | road |
| known | sewn | yolk | foam | folk |
| rope | sown | close (verb) | ghost | throat |
| soap | froze | close (adj.) | toast | wrote |
| mauve | chose | gross | loth/loath | growth |
| hoax | foes | thrown | loathe | oath |
| whole | roll | throne | soul | sloth |
| bowl | coal | shoal | volt | mould |

We have called this sound OU, but in fact it is also quite frequently spelt OW, as you can see in these words:— *cow, growl, crowd, brown; cloud, sound, shout, ouch.*

You have to be slightly careful with OW words, as OW can spell a different sound — as in: *blow, slow, grown* (the OE sound that we have just covered on Factsheet Eight).

OU as a combination of letters is a real horror though. Just look at these words:— *rough, cough, mould; four, ought; group.* They are spelt OU, but they all have different sounds! And they do not include the most common OU words, those we are dealing with on this page, like *loud, sound, mouth.* The only thing to be done with these words is keep your own lists of ones that give you problems, and make a real effort to learn them.

In the Wordlist below, try to concentrate on which words have the OU spelling, and which have OW. The 'clues' are designed to help in this direction.

## WORDLIST

| | | | | | |
|---|---|---|---|---|---|
| how | (normally OW) | brown | (normally OWN) | house | (OUSE) |
| | | noun | (the exception) | house | (*to house*, verb) |
| bough | (branch) | | | | |
| bow | (verb, *to bend*) | round | (normally OUND) | douse | (to put out/throw water on) |
| | | wound | (from *to wind*) | dowse | (search for water) |
| plough | (OUGH) | crowned | (from *to crown*) | | |
| slough | (OUGH) | | | clout | (OUT) |
| | | count | (OU) | | |
| thou | (OU) | | | doubt | (silent B) |
| | | sour | (OUR) | | |
| couch | (always OUCH) | | | drought | (OUGHT) |
| | | hour | (time) | | |
| cloud | (usually OUD) | our | (belongs to us) | mouth | OUTH |
| crowd | (except *crowd*) | | | mouth | (*to mouth*, verb) |
| | | bower | (OWER) | | |
| howl | (usually OWL) | cower | | blouse | (OU) |
| owl | | dower | | rouse | |
| | | power | | | |
| foul | (OU: unpleasant) | tower | | browse | (OW) |
| fowl | (bird) | | | | |
| | | flour | (white powder) | | |
| bowel | (OWEL) | flower | (plant) | | |
| dowel | | | | | |
| rowel | | *Note:* Words ending in *our* and *ower* | | | |
| towel | | really have two syllables. | | | |
| trowel | | | | | |
| vowel | | | | | |

# THE OI SOUND

Because the OU Wordlist is relatively short, we have space on this Factsheet to look at another sound based on the letter O:— O plus I, or O plus Y, as in:— *joy, toys, soil, point.*

The OY spelling appears at the end of words (unless an S has been added, or perhaps an ED to make the past tense of a verb). There are not many short words ending in OY, but quite a few longer ones.

The other short words are all spelt with an OI, as you will see from the Wordlist.

## WORDLIST

| | | | | | |
|---|---|---|---|---|---|
| boy | (young man) | void | (space | choice | (CE) |
| buoy | (in the sea) | | | voice | |
| | | boil | (heat water/a blister) | | |
| cloy | | | | moist | |
| coy | | spoil | | | |
| joy | | spoilt | | quoit | |
| toy | | | | | |
| | | join | | noise | (SE) |
| | | joint | | poise | |
| | | | | | |
| | | | | toys | |

## EXERCISES

The exercises and spelling tests include both OU and OI words.

a) For each question find a pair of homophones to fill the gaps in each pair of sentences. The ones you need are in the Wordlists.

(1) Carefully John clambered out along the swaying ............ of the tree.
I call upon you all to ............ your heads in a silent prayer.

(2) The flashing light of the marker ............ told us the harbour was near.
Which ............ is responsible for putting this cobra in my desk?

(3) If you water that ............ any more it will have to swim to the side of its pot.
Take six tablespoons of white ............ and beat in the egg yolks.

(4) Out of the vast and reeking pit a ............ stench arose as if from the depths of Hell itself.
A tender young ............ always makes a tasty meal.

(5) ............ house is the one with the yellow door and purple curtains; you can't miss it.
The church clock counted out each passing ............ through the night. (10)

b) Rewrite these sentences, correcting the wrongly spelt OU and OI words.

(1) The attempt to douse for water produced no luck; we only struck oyle.

(2) I heard a houl of pain as dad tripped over the toise we had left on the stairs.

(3) The army marched three times rownd the tour, sounding their trumpets.

(4) From outside the palace gates the king could hear the nois of an ever-growing croud, angrily demanding that he should answer their grievances.

(5) The plow cut swiftly through the moised and yielding soil. (10)

c) All of the following words are spelt OU, but only half of them have the OU SOUND. Divide them into two lists: those with the OU sound, and those with other sounds.

| | | | | | | | | | |
|---|---|---|---|---|---|---|---|---|---|
| louse | cough | four | bounce | shout | ought | hound | spout | group | scour |
| trough | south | court | youth | rouse | your | ouch | moult | proud | through (20) |

d) Write out the following sentences, inserting the correct spelling from the choice of three you are given in brackets. Underline the word you use.

(1) She delivered her speech with considerable (poice, poise, poys).

(2) "(Dows, dowse, douse) that light! Don't you know there's a war on . . .?"

(3) Mr Slope entered with the usual (sower, soure, sour) expression on his face, and announced that we were going to have a spelling test.

(4) Jack was obviously stuck, so I tried to (mouthe, mouth, mowth) the answer to him.

(5) Unfortunately Mr Slope saw me and gave a (showt, shout, shoute) of anger.

(6) While I was being deafened by the (sounde, sound, sownd) of the teacher's voice, Jack managed to copy the answer from Mary.

(7) I have told you before not to (bounce, bounse, bownse) on that sofa.

(8) For seven years the land was ravaged by a terrible (drout, drowt, drought).

(9) "Are you sure you've washed your hands, Tony?" "Yes, mum, just look at the (towle, toul, towel)."

(10) I have no (dought, doute, doubt) that you will all do well in this exercise. (10)

## SPELLING TESTS

| 1 | 2 | 3 | 4 | 5 |
|---|---|---|---|---|
| bough | plough | slough | thou | row (= noise) |
| bow (verb) | crowd | foul | shroud | couch |
| cowl | cloud | fowl | gown | scowl |
| vowel | bound | ground | noun | towel |
| bounce | crowned | drown | hour | ounce |
| spouse | flower | count | our | doubt |
| wound (verb) | flour | bout | tower | drought |
| boy | rout | joys | voice | spout |
| buoy | void | noise | spoilt | frown |
| moist | toyed | coin | choice | quoit |

The words on this page present many more problems. They fall into two groups:— those with a R in the spelling (like *lord*, *roar*, *sore*); and those that are spelt AU or AW, (like *law*, *drawn*, *haunt* and *launch*).

It is not always possible to tell apart words like *raw* and *roar*, *paw* and *poor* — and the result is an enormous number of groups of homophones.

There are also many odd little variations in spelling that you need to watch out for (such as the AR spelling in *war* and *warn*; AL in *chalk* and ALL in *hall*; GHT in *caught* and *bought*).

In the Wordlist particular problems are noted for you, but there are many different spellings to learn, and you would be sensible to make your own list of problem words and concentrate on those (as you have been advised earlier).

## WORDLIST

| | | | | | |
|---|---|---|---|---|---|
| boar | (OA: pig) | daub | (AU: paint) | storm | (OR: gale) |
| bore | (ORE: drill) | orb | (OR: globe) | warm | (AR: hot) |
| caw | (AW: rook) | torch | (OR: light) | born | (OR: baby) |
| core | (ORE: apple) | board | (OAR: plank/lodging) | borne | (silent E: carried) |
| corps | (! army unit) | bored | (ORE: weary) | dawn | (AW: morning) |
| door | (OOR) | broad | (OA: wide) | torn | (OR: ripped) |
| draw | (AW: pencil) | cord | (OR: string) | morn | (OR: = morning) |
| drawer | (AWER: container) | chord | (! music) | mourn | (OUR: grieve) |
| flaw | AW: fault) | fraud | (AU: deceit) | yawn | (AW: sleepy) |
| floor | (OOR: ground) | hoard | (OAR: to store) | launch | (always AUNCH: boat) |
| for | (OR: because) | horde | (OR: crowd) | haunt | (always AUNT: ghost) |
| fore | (ORE: front) | sawed | (AW: cut) | coarse | (OAR: rough) |
| four | (OUR: number) | soared | (OAR: flew) | course | (OUR: track) |
| law | (AW: rules) | sword | (! weapon) | force | (CE: strength) |
| lore | (ORE: legend) | ward | (AR: hospital) | horse | (SE: animal) |
| moor | (OOR: hill) | dwarf | (AR: small) | sauce | (AU: flavour) |
| more | (ORE: extra) | wharf | (AR: jetty) | source | (OUR: origin) |
| nor | (OR: not) | forge | (OR: make) | bought | (! buy) |
| gnaw | (! chew) | fork | (OR: prongs) | brought | (! bring) |
| oar | (OAR: boat) | hawk | (AW: bird) | caught | (! catch) |
| or | (OR: alternative) | talk | (AL: speak) | court | (OUR: judge) |
| ore | (ORE: metal) | walk | (AL: move) | fought | (! fight) |
| paw | (AW: foot) | ball | (ALL: round) | fort | (OR: castle) |
| poor | (OOR: not rich) | bawl | (AWL: cry) | ought | (! must) |
| pore | (ORE: little hole) | call | (ALL: shout) | sought | (! from *to seek*) |
| pour | (OUR: flow) | hall | (ALL: room) | sort | (OR: type) |
| raw | (AW: uncooked) | haul | (AUL: drag) | taught | (GHT: teach) |
| roar | (OAR: snarl) | pall | (ALL: shroud) | taut | (AU: stretched tight) |
| shore | (ORE: coast) | Paul | (AUL: the name) | wart | (AR: spot) |
| sure | (URE: certain) | shawl | (AWL: cloth) | forth | (OR: 'looked forth') |
| saw | (AW: see) | trawl | (AWL: to fish) | fourth | (OUR: 4) |
| soar | (OAR: fly) | small | (ALL: little) | quartz | (! rock) |
| sore | (ORE: hurt) | squall | (ALL: gust) | cause | (AU: reason) |
| tore | (ORE: tear) | tall | (ALL: high) | clause | (AU: sentence) |
| tour | (OUR: trip) | wall | (ALL: bricks) | claws | (AW: from *claw*) |
| war | (AR: fight) | bald | (AL: no hair) | gauze | (AU: thin material) |
| wore | (ORE: wear) | bawled | (AW: cried) | pause | (AU: halt) |
| yore | (ORE: olden) | | | paws | (AW: from *paw*) |
| your | (OUR: you) | | | | |

*Notice also* halt *and* salt (AL), vault (AUL) *and* waltz (!) *which have different pronunciations in different parts of the* country.

NOTE: Where a word has a really strange spelling, there is an exclamation mark (!) to warn you; otherwise the *key letters* in the word are given, together with a 'clue word' as usual.

**EXERCISES**

(a) In each of the following sentences there are two missing words; and in each case they are a pair of homophones. Write out the sentences inserting the correctly spelt word in each gap from the choices given you.

(1) A ............ of people were clambering over the golden ............ of the dead dragon. (hord, hoard, hoared, hored, horde, hourde)

(2) As soon as she saw her uncle's ............ head, the baby ............ at the top of her voice. (bawld, balled, bald, bawled, baled, balde)

(3) "In this case, m'lud, I have ............ to show what ............ of a man the defendant really is." (sourt, sought, sorte, sort, soughrt, sored)

(4) With a savage ............ the lion sprang upon the ............ meat. (rore, roar, roare, rawer, raw, raur)

(5) Even ............ police now joined the search for the escaped convict across the wilds of the ............ . (more, moar, mawer, mour, moor, maur)

(6) Not all soldiers in the Middle Ages ............ heavy suits of armour when they went to ............ . (woor, woar, waur, wore, war, whaur)

(7) Due to ............ in the materials used to manufacture the concrete ............, the entire block must be demolished. (flause, flors, floors, flaws, flawse, flores)

(8) Though the defenders ............ bravely, the ............ finally fell to its attackers. (faught, fort, fought, foret, fawt, thought)

(9) Adam was ............ at home, and wanted to ............ at his school. (bored, bord, boared, board, bawd, boured)

(10) Slade went in with the score at one hundred runs ............ ............ wickets. (fore, faur, fower, faw, for, four)

(20)

(b) Make a list of all of the different spellings for the OR/AU sound that you can find. You will need to go through the Wordlist very carefully! For each different spelling give two different examples (unless only one word is spelt that way!)

(10)

(c) Each question consists of a pair of sentences, from which a pair of homophones is missing. You are not told anything about the missing words, but you should be able to work them out from the sentences, and by using the Wordlist.

(1) We ............ for our fallen companion.
The earliest light of dewy ............ bedecks the boughs.

(2) The ............ cloth rubbed painfully against his wounds.
The ............ is three miles long, with twenty-one fences.

(3) The rope stretched ............ across the ravine.
Has no-one ever ............ you how to spell properly?

(4) The convict has finally been ............ by the police.
The inner ............-yard was surrounded by walls and towers.

(5) Playfully the kitten ............ the ball of wool.
Water ............ in a torrent from the broken dam.

(10)

(d) Use each of the following words in a sentence of its own, so that its meaning is clear from the way you have used it:—

sauce    source    tore    tour    nor    gnaw    boar    bore    shore    sure

(10)

## SPELLING TESTS

| 1 | 2 | 3 | 4 | 5 |
|---|---|---|---|---|
| bored | nor | paw | force | sword |
| board | gnaw | pore | horse | sawed |
| cork | scorn | poor | trawl | soared |
| stalk | warn | pour | haul | hawk |
| dwarf | yawn | forge | squall | stork |
| haunt | mourn | gauze | quart | chord |
| course | sauce | sought | jaw | daub |
| coarse | source | sort | dawn | vault |
| clause | sores | taught | shore | halt |
| claws | saws | taut | sure | ought |

Double O spells yet another different sound, as you can hear in words like: *food, cool, moon.*
There is no great problem with this sound or this spelling, though you do need to remember that OO can spe[ll] other sounds (as in *good, wool, door).*
There are also, of course, several alternative spellings:— OU (in *group),* OUGH (in *through),* O by itself (in *tom[b]* and *who),* O with a silent E (in *prove).*
The main alternative spelling, however, is with the letter U, which is not surprising, as OO is really a long [U] sound.
So we get UE (as in *clue),* and U plus a silent E (as in *rude).*
There is yet a third common spelling for this sound:— EW as in *flew* and *threw.*
And of course you must always watch out for the 'odd' spellings.

## WORDLIST

| | | | | | |
|---|---|---|---|---|---|
| blew | (from *blow*) | fluke | (U plus E) | boost | (OO) |
| blue | (colour) | spook | (OO) | root | (plant) |
| brew | (EW) | cool | (OO) | route | (way) |
| chew | | fool | | brute | (U plus E) |
| crew | | cruel | (UE) | flute | |
| drew | | gruel | | fruit | (UI) |
| grew | | rule | (U plus E) | suit | |
| screw | | school | (silent H) | loot | (plunder) |
| shrew | | ghoul | (silent H) | lute | (instrument) |
| slew | | doom | (OO) | shoot | (fire!) |
| clue | (UE) | gloom | | chute | (slide) |
| glue | | plume | (U plus E) | sleuth | (EU) |
| rue | | whom | (O) | tooth | (OO) |
| sue | | tomb | (silent B) | truth | (U) |
| true | | womb | (silent B) | youth | (OU) |
| do | (O) | moon | (OO) | smooth | (no E) |
| who | | soon | | soothe | (E) |
| shoe | (on foot) | prune | (U plus E) | groove | (OO) |
| shoo | (go away!) | strewn | (EW) | move | (O plus E) |
| threw | (from *throw*) | hoop | (OO) | prove | |
| through | (across) | loop | | choose | (OO) |
| to | (towards) | group | (OU) | ooze | (Z) |
| too | (very) | soup | | snooze | (Z) |
| two | (number) | troop | (of soldiers) | bruise | (UI) |
| woo | (OO) | troupe | (of acrobats) | cruise | |
| zoo | | goose | (OO) | lose | (lost) |
| food | (OO) | loose | (not tight) | whose | |
| mood | | juice | (UI) | ruse | (U plus E) |
| rude | (U plus E) | sluice | | shoes | (OE) |
| shrewd | (EW) | spruce | (U plus E) | trews | (trousers) |
| hoof | (OO) | truce | | | |

In addition to the above words, there is a second group. They have the same spellings, but a rather different sound. Instead of OO, they sound like YOO! Read a few of them, to see what is meant:— *cue, few, tune, news, cure.*

Here is the full list:—

| | | | | | | | |
|---|---|---|---|---|---|---|---|
| cue | (snooker) | view | (IE) | fugue | (music) | use | (noun and verb) |
| queue | (line) | yew | (tree) | duke | | used | |
| dew | (water) | you | (not me) | duel | (fight) | mute | |
| due | (owing) | ewe | (sheep) | jewel | (gem) | newt | |
| Jew | (Jewish) | tube | | mule | | fuse | |
| hew | (to cut) | feud | (EU) | fume | | news | |
| hue | (colour) | lewd | (EW) | dupe | | mews | (stable block) |
| few | (EW) | nude | (U plus E) | cure | | muse | (to think) |

# EXERCISES

(a) In the following short passage from a story of espionage, some of the words have been deliberately mis-spelt. Write out the passage, correcting the mistakes.

> "Chute the man in the green suite". That was the order that had been given to our groope. I was the only one to make it thru the guards. The chief of the Secret Police had been two shroud for us. The lute was already being loaded into the yacht, and it was not a pleasure crews for El Presidente with all his ill-gotten gains. His crewel rool was over at last, but he did not plan to leave empty-handed. (10)

(b) In each of the following sentences, you have to find a pair of homophones to go into the two gaps. Make sure you put the right homophone into the right gap!
  (1)  Jim ............ the ball straight ............ the window.
  (2)  The North Wind ............ cold and strong, and our noses all turned ............ .
  (3)  The two cavaliers fought a ............ over the queen's ............ .*
  (4)  I will wait for ............ tonight, there beside the old ............ tree.
  (5)  Go over ............ the hatch and collect our meals, while I find a table and ............ chairs for us. (10)

*The two words you need here are not *quite* homophones in fact!

(c) Make two lists of your own, of words that have the OO or YOO sound. The first list is to contain ten words spelt with a double O. The second list is to contain ten words which are spelt with a U followed by a SILENT E on the end of the word. BUT — you are not allowed to use any word that appears in the Wordlists opposite! (10)

(d) In this exercise, each sentence contains two OO/YOO words for which you have to choose the correct spelling. You are given a choice of three for each of them, in the brackets. Write out the sentences and underline the correct spellings which you have used.

  (1)  Here, drink this hot (soop, soup, soupe), dear, and you'll (sune, soon, sewn) be feeling better.
  (2)  When you've finished it, I'll bring you some nice (proon, prewn, prune) (juce, juice, joose).
  (3)  Fearfully we entered the (glume, gloom, glewm) of the vampire's (toom, tome, tomb).
  (4)  Suddenly the (bume, bewm, boom) of a great drum beating out a grim (tune, tewn, toon) shattered the silence.
  (5)  Now we (knew, new, niou) that somewhere in the depths the (goul, ghoul, gowel) was waiting for us.
  (6)  I took off my (shoes, shose, shos) for a quiet (snoose, snuze, snooze).
  (7)  Rather like a tram, he only (mooves, moves, muves) in fixed (grooves, groves, gruves).
  (8)  The old woman chased the (yuthes, yewths, youths) waving her (brume, broom, bruim).
  (9)  Anyone who breaks the (rools, rules, rewels) here is (dumed, dombed, doomed) to a fate worse than death.
  (10)  We always have (grool, greul, gruel) for our dinners at (skule, shcool, school). (20)

# SPELLING TESTS

| 1 | 2 | 3 | 4 | 5 |
|---|---|---|---|---|
| blue | dew | through | to | queue |
| blew | do | threw | two | cue |
| flute | due | room | too | jewel |
| fruit | crude | whom | sleuth | duel |
| route | food | tomb | youth | whose |
| root | shrewd | fume | tooth | shoes |
| duke | feud | group | mule | choose |
| spook | view | droop | school | bruise |
| noose | truce | dupe | ghoul | ooze |
| knew | sluice | stew | fuel | news |

We have just seen one sort of U sound (what we might call 'LONG U') spelt with double O. There is another, short, U SOUND, spelt with the letter U. You can recognise it in words like: *such, club, pump, sunk, up* and *crust*.

There are some other spellings of this sound:— OO in *blood* and *flood* (which you would expect to make the OO sound you find in *mood* and *food*); O by itself in *won* and *ton*; O with a silent E in *come* and *done*; — and several others. But the number of such words is quite small.

## WORDLIST

| | | | | | |
|---|---|---|---|---|---|
| club | | come | (O plus E) | rung | (ladder/from *ring* (bells)) |
| rub | | drum | | wrung | (twisted; from *wring*) |
| clutch | (TCH) | swum | | tongue | (GUE) |
| Dutch | | crumb | (silent B) | young | (OU) |
| much | (CH) | numb | | plunge | (U) |
| such | | thumb | | sponge | (O) |
| touch | | plum | (fruit) | junk | (usually UNK) |
| mud | | plumb | (a lead weight) | trunk | |
| blood | | some | (any) | monk | (O — the exception) |
| flood | | sum | (add up) | hunt | (usually UNT) |
| bluff | | jump | | front | (O — the exception) |
| stuff | | plump | | cup | |
| ruff | (collar) | mumps | | bus | |
| rough | (not smooth) | bun | | us | |
| tough | | run | | fuss | (double S) |
| tuft | | done | (finished) | brush | |
| rug | | dun | (brown) | gush | |
| snug | | none | (not any) | dusk | (usually USK) |
| fudge | (DGE) | nun | (lady monk) | brusque | (except this odd word) |
| luck | (CK) | son | (child) | crust | |
| stuck | | sun | (light) | dust | |
| ducked | (from *to duck*) | ton | (a weight) | but | (however) |
| duck | (bird/stoop) | tonne | (metric tonne) | butt | (hit with head) |
| dull | | tun | (a barrel) | shut | (usually one T) |
| skull | | won | (from *win*) | putt | (in golf; double T) |
| gulch | | one | (single) | dove | (OVE) |
| bulge | | lunch | | glove | |
| sulk | | munch | | love | |
| gulp | | fund | | shove | |
| sculpt | | flung | | crux | |
| pulse | | strung | | buzz | |
| cult | | | | does | |

There is another sound similar to the above, but not quite the same. We have called it **UH**; you can hear it in these words: *could, stood, took*. (Compare them with: *cud, stud* and *tuck*!) These words are spelt with OO (*good*), U (*bull*) or OU (*would*). Here is their list:—

| | | | | | |
|---|---|---|---|---|---|
| could | (silent L) | book | (Notice all | bull | (U) |
| should | | brook | these K words) | full | |
| would | (might) | cook | | pull | |
| wood | (tree) | crook | | wool | (OO) |
| | | hook | | wolf | (O) |
| hood | | look | | bush | |
| stood | | rook | | push | |
| | | shook | | foot | (OO) |
| | | took | | soot | |
| | | | | put | (U) |

## EXERCISES

a) This is a homophones exercise, of the sort you are now used to. For each pair of sentences find a suitable pair of homophones from the Wordlists, and insert them in the gaps.

(1) Round his neck the courtier wore a white starched ............ .
Outside the school gate some nasty ........... boys were waiting to jump on poor little Clarence.

(2) Mrs Jumbly, who already has seven daughters, is hoping that this time her new baby will be a ............ .
Above us the ........... blazed relentlessly down on the scorching desert.

(3) You may have ........... our battle of wits this time, Moriarty, but there will be another day.
Finally, only ........... remained of the three Musketeers.

(4) They said that they ............ like to attend, but were unable to do so because of a prior engagement.
Your problem is that you can't see the ........... for the trees.

(5) With a shout of joy he slapped me on the back, then ........... my hand repeatedly in his vice-like grip.
She climbed carefully up the rickety old ladder, testing each ........... before she put her weight on it.     (10)

b) Find from the Wordlist opposite, and make a note of, each of the following:—

(1) Three words with a silent L
(2) Four words with a silent B
(3) One word with a silent W
(4) One word ending in GUE
(5) One word ending in QUE     (10)

c) Write down a word that RHYMES with each of the following:—

| wool | front | young | come | tough |
| love | buzz | clutch | son | fuss |     (10)

d) In the following passage there are twenty words with the SHORT U or UH sound. Ten of them have been spelt correctly, ten have been spelt incorrectly. Write out the passage, correcting the mistakes, and underlining ALL twenty words, the right ones as well as the wrong ones. Then make two lists, firstly of the ten words you have corrected, then of the ten words that were already right.

The silence of death houng over the abbey as dusk turned to night and hid away the deeds of day. The bells wrung no more. The front of the great church lay ruined in the dust. The soote from the fires of ancient books was black under foot. The windows had been flongue down, their glass all smashed. Where wonce the voices of the munks had sung, the wild wolfs now cud howl beneath the moon. The trunks of trees would jut through lumpse of stone, and rain and wind wood sculpt new figures from the images of saints.     (20)

## SPELLING TESTS

| 1 | 2 | 3 | 4 | 5 |
| --- | --- | --- | --- | --- |
| such | blood | rough | fudge | done |
| touch | scud | bluff | struck | sun |
| clutch | numb | dumb | thumb | son |
| flood | some | once | sponge | tongue |
| could | sum | does | would | bulge |
| hood | drum | lungs | wood | wrung |
| front | bush | wolf | cult | rung |
| crook | soot | wool | sculpt | young |
| tough | put | pull | pulse | glove |
| cuff | putt | crux | brusque | crumb |

This sound is probably nearer to U than to anything else. It is the sound you make when you are not sure:—
"*Er* . . . I think that's right . . . Well, *er*, let me see."

On the other hand, it is the basic vowel sound in a surprisingly large number of words, and it has several alternative spellings, as you will see from these notes, and the Wordlist:—

UR in many words, such as:— *blur, fur, spur, church, curl, burn, hurt, curse.*

ER is also common, as in:— *her, verb, term, fern, stern, verse, nerve.*

IR may be even more common, as in:— *fir, birch, bird, first, dirt, birth.*

OR turns up in a few words:— *word, work, worm, worst.*

EAR surprisingly enough also makes the ER/UR sound:— *search, heard, learn, earth.*

And what about YR in myrrh (one of the gifts of the Three Wise Men)?

The only thing all these spellings have in common is the letter R, and with so many alternatives there are quite a few pairs of homophones.

The Wordlist once again links related words and gives some 'key letters' as well as 'clue words'. Nevertheless, there is a fair amount of learning to be done with these words.

## WORDLIST

| | | | | | |
|---|---|---|---|---|---|
| blur | (UR) | dirge | (I: sad tune) | fern | (E) |
| cur | (dog) | merge | (E: join) | stern | |
| slur | (insult) | verge | (edge) | learn | (EA) |
| spur | | serge | (E: rough cloth) | yearn | (to long for) |
| err | (E: mistake) | surge | (U: movement) | chirp | (I: birdsong) |
| fir | (I: tree) | purge | (U: get rid of) | curse | (U) |
| fur | (U: on animal) | urge | | nurse | |
| her | (E) | dirk | (I: Scots dagger) | purse | |
| sir | (I) | kirk | (I: Scots church) | hearse | (EA: funeral car) |
| stir | | quirk | (oddity) | verse | (E) |
| purr | (U) | jerk | (E) | terse | (brief) |
| whirr | (I) | perk | (benefit) | worse | (O) |
| myrrh | (!) | lurk | (U) | burst | (U) |
| curb | (U: restrain) | work | (O) | first | (I) |
| kerb | (E: pavement) | curl | (U) | thirst | |
| herb | (E) | furl | (roll up) | worst | (O) |
| verb | | hurl | | blurt | (U: shout out) |
| birch | (I) | pearl | (EA: jewel) | curt | (short) |
| smirch | (smear) | purl | (U: knitting!) | hurt | |
| church | (U) | earl | (EA: lord) | spurt | (sudden rush) |
| lurch | (stagger) | girl | (I) | dirt | (I) |
| perch | (E) | twirl | | flirt | |
| search | (EA) | whirl | (spin) | shirt | |
| bird | (I) | whirled | (spun) | squirt | |
| gird | (to put on) | world | (O: the earth) | skirt | |
| heard | (EA: listened) | firm | (I) | birth | (I: being born) |
| herd | (E: animals) | squirm | (wriggle) | berth | (E: dock) |
| word | (O) | term | (E) | earth | (EA) |
| curds | (U: 'and whey') | worm | (O) | mirth | (I) |
| serf | (E: peasant) | burn | (U) | worth | (O) |
| surf | (U: sea-shore) | churn | (milk) | curve | (U) |
| turf | | spurn | (reject) | nerve | (E) |
| | | earn | (EA: wages) | serve | |
| | | urn | (U: large pot) | swerve | |

## EXERCISES

(a) Do you remember the extract from the spy story on Worksheet Eleven? Here is another piece of it. Once again there are some words spelt incorrectly, and your task is to rewrite the passage correcting the mistakes.

> The bullet struck the kirb beside the main road into the dockyard. A spert of stone chippings flew up into my face. That was only the furst shot of many. A sudden birst of automatic fire word harmlessly over my head. I swirved round the corner of a grain warehouse, and hit the dert. In hur birth, the presidential yacht blazed furiously. Whatever happened to me now, I knew that the whirled was free from the tyrant.                                    (10)

(b) This is the usual 'spot the homophones' exercise. Each of the following sentences contains two gaps, in which you are to insert a pair of homophones that make sense. You will find the words you need in the list opposite.

    (1) The animal cleans itself by rubbing its ............ against the rough bark of the ............ tree.

    (2) Every penny he ............ he hides away in one of a whole array of clay ............ which are concealed in the cellars of his house.

    (3) Are we really to believe that this solid ............ is ............ about the sun like some child's spinning top?

    (4) Putting my ear to the ground, I ............ the distant sound of a ............ of stampeding buffalo.

    (5) I caught sight of him briefly, still wearing his old-fashioned ............ suit, before a sudden ............ of the crowd towards the barriers separated us again.                                    (10)

(c) Make a list of all the words from the Wordlist opposite that end with a SILENT E. The silent E is there for a reason — and it is not the same reason that we find a silent E on words like *bone, lane, pine*. At the end of your list, write, in a couple of sentences, an explanation of what the silent E is doing on these (and many other similar) words.                                    (10)

(d) In the following sentences you are given a choice of possible spellings for several ER/UR words. Rewrite the sentences inserting the correct spelling from the alternatives provided in the brackets.

    (1) His (virse, verse, vurse) is some of the (worse, worst, wurst) poetry I have ever read.

    (2) "Please, (sir, sire, cur), Jimmy keeps trying to (skwert, squrt, squirt) ink on to my book."

    (3) "Jimmy, go and sit with the (gurls, gerls, girls), and don't even (stur, ster, stir) a finger for the rest of this lesson."

    (4) The (furst, ferst, first) thing I (herd, heared, heard) when I awoke was the (churp, chirp, cherp) of a little (bird, beard, berd) in the tree.

    (5) There was I, waiting at the (cherch, chirch, church), when I found he'd left me in the (lirch, lurch, lerch).

    (6) How did you get all that (durt, dert, dirt) on your (shirt, sheart, shurt), child?

    (7) His (wurds, werds, words) (merged, murged, mirjed) into a continuous drone, and his face became a (blur, blir, blurr) as I slipped into unconsciousness.

    (8) The (terf, tirf, turf) fire of the croft (burnt, bearnt, birnt) merrily in the grate, and the thick smoke (cirled, curled, cearlt) round the rafters.                                    (20)

## SPELLING TESTS

| 1 | 2 | 3 | 4 | 5 |
|---|---|---|---|---|
| thirst | heard | earl | earth | murk |
| herb | herd | curl | worth | work |
| turf | purl | girl | birth | quirk |
| fir | pearl | urge | berth | firm |
| fur | twirl | verge | serge | curve |
| hearse | world | dirge | surge | swerve |
| verse | birch | curb | purr | yearn |
| worse | church | kerb | stir | spurn |
| worst | search | earn | slur | stern |
| burst | perch | urn | whirr | myrrh |

This Factsheet contains some reminders and rules about CONSONANT sounds at the ends of words. For the first time we will also begin to look at some longer words as well, and see how the rules apply to them.

### C, K and CK

We find CK at the end of words when it follows a SINGLE vowel:— *smack, stick, attack, o'clock.*

We find K at the end, without any C, when it follows two vowels together, and also when it follows another consonant:— *steak, peak, oak, look,* and *talk, sink, lark, murk.*

When there is a silent E on the end, there is never a C with the K:— *flake, like, smoke.*

Be careful of the large number of long words that end in IC:— *comic, critic, drastic, arctic, catholic, electric, lunatic, romantic, arithmetic, Pacific, Atlantic, politics, mathematics.*

There are also a few others words ending in C (*zinc, maniac*) and some real oddities (*plaque, ache*).

### GE and J

The letter J does not appear at the ends of words. At the end of words this sound is spelt GE (*siege, range* and *arrange*) or DGE when it is following a SINGLE SHORT vowel sound (*cadge, edge, bridge* — and *knowledge*). *But notice the common AGE ending* — *sausage, carriage,* etc.

### CH and TCH

Once again, after a SHORT SINGLE vowel, it is usually TCH:— *catch, wretch, Scotch, hutch,* — EXCEPT in *attach, detach* and *enrich.* (*Despatch* and *bewitch* 'obey the rule', though!). Following another consonant, or two vowels together, it is just CH:— *each, poach* and *research.*

### VE not V

V at the end of a word is ALWAYS followed by an E:— *have, sieve, leave, love, groove.*

### F, L, S and Z

After a SINGLE vowel these four consonants are nearly always DOUBLED at the end of a word; but not after a a pair of vowels, or after a consonant:— *cliff, staff; pull, will; kiss, press;* — but *reef, roof; coal, peel.*

And remember that the S and Z sound at the end of words is very often spelt CE or SE:— *face, place, mice; loose; cheese* and *sneeze.* You find the CE and SE spelling in many longer words too:— *disgrace, replace, surface* (ACE is the usual spelling); *decrease* and *release* (EASE); *advice, precise, paradise, sacrifice* (ICE, or ISE); *arose, oppose, suppose* (there are many words ending in POSE); *amuse* and *excuse* (USE).

The Wordlist that follows contains some more examples in addition to those mentioned, particularly the longer and more difficult examples! Of course there are many more that could have been included. Remember to keep your own list of words *you* find difficult.

## WORDLIST

| C, K and CK | | VE | S and Z — SE and CE | | |
|---|---|---|---|---|---|
| lilac | attic | forgave | circus (one S) | dismiss | amaze |
| almanac | antic | forgive | focus (one S) | crisis (one S) | amuse |
| havoc | arctic | relieve | harass | notice | excuse |
| mistake | caustic | deceive | surpass | service | increase |
| mistook | chronic | dissolve | amass | lettuce | disease |
| overtake | hectic | approve | address | advice | reverse |
| dislike | artistic | | actress | advise | rehearse |
| provoke | dramatic | GE | princess | device | defence |
| remark | magnetic | orange | countless | devise | silence |
| monarch (!CH) | majestic | syringe | hopeless | surprise | violence |
| antique | mechanic | baggage | sickness | disguise (U !) | expense |
| oblique | narcotic | sausage | madness | | convince. |
| | nomadic | marriage | | exercise | |
| | pathetic | revenge | | rejoice | |
| | picnic (C) | | | | |
| | picnicked (CK) | | | | |

This Wordlist is only intended to be a first introduction to some of the longer words. We will cover most of them again in more detail, so do not worry if you find it hard at this stage. Even so, you should find that what you have learnt so far is already helping you out!

## EXERCISES

(a) Write out the following sentences, inserting the correct spelling from the choices you are given in the brackets.

(1) I have (noticed, notised, notissed) an improvement in your (arithmetick, arithmetic, arithmetik) lately, Joanne.

(2) So my (advise, advize, advice) is to (practise, practice, practize) your spelling instead.

(3) Only a (maniak, maniack, maniac) would have made the (plaque, plac, plack) from (zink, zinc, zinck) instead of brass.

(4) If I (catch, cach, cache) the (rech, wrech, wretch) who is responsible he will get a good (smacke, smack, smak).

(10)

(b) Write a sentence or two of your own to *explain* the difference between the two words in each of the following pairs:—

| (1) practise practice | (2) advice advise | (3) devise device | (4) lose loose | (5) price prize |
|---|---|---|---|---|

(10)

(c) In the passage that follows, twenty words have been printed in *italics*. Rewrite the passage, correcting the words that are spelt wrong. But be careful. Only ten of the twenty are wrong; the others are right!

"I can never *forgive* you, Lady. You have *decieved* me too often. There can be no *excuse* for what you have done today. *Once* you were my *princes*. Now your *disguize* has been *replased* by your true *face*. How can you stand there in *silense*? Have you no *defence*, nothing to *convinse* me that I have made a *drastik mistake*? — No, do not *pul* my *sleeve*. Do not try to *kis* my feet. *Leave* my sight forever in *disgrase*."

"Oh, don't be so *dramatic*, George. She's only eaten your *sausages*, and she is only a dog . . ."

(10)

(d) For this exercise, you have to think of some words that are not in the Wordlist, or on the Factsheet at all. You have to complete the lists with words that are spelt in a similar way. Words given you opposite are not allowed, nor are one-syllable (single sound) words. The letter combinations that must appear in your words are given to you, together with the number of new words you have to find. For example:—

| Reduce | induce | deduce | introduce | UCE (2) |
|---|---|---|---|---|

| | | | | | |
|---|---|---|---|---|---|
| (1) | Oppose | suppose | ............ | ............ | ............ | OSE (3) |
| (2) | Attic | dramatic | ............ | ............ | ............ | TIC (3) |
| (3) | Amuse | excuse | ............ | ............ | ............ | USE (3) |
| (4) | Replace | necklace | ............ | ............ | ............ | ACE (3) |
| (5) | Relieve | reprieve | ............ | ............ | | IEVE (2) |
| (6) | Deceive | perceive | ............ | ............ | | EIVE (2) |
| (7) | Baggage | courage | ............ | ............ | | |
| | | | ............ | ............ | | AGE (4) |

(20)

## SPELLING TESTS

| 1 | 2 | 3 | 4 | 5 |
|---|---|---|---|---|
| stick | speak | attack | comic | link |
| stake | this | focus | harass | caustic |
| book | hiss | orange | address | silence |
| chronic | syringe | electric | soak | expense |
| circus | picnic | spark | smoke | break |
| attic | overtake | lettuce | walk | dismiss |
| remark | cheese | suppose | mechanic | crisis |
| monarch | sneeze | release | surface | paradise |
| excuse | advice | relieve | antique | havoc |
| lilac | advise | violence | oblique | attach |

This Factsheet is partly about adding endings, particularly ED and ING, to words; but also about when you find DOUBLE consonants, — and when you don't.

The basic rule about double consonants in the middle of words is this:— After a SINGLE SHORT VOWEL (A, E, I, O, U by themselves, and making their own ordinary sound) you usually find a DOUBLE rather than a single consonant. Look at these examples:—

*ladder* (short A sound, so double D); *settle* (short E sound, so double T); *kitten* (short I sound, so double T); *bottom* (short O sound, so double T again); *stubborn* (short U sound, so double B); similarly — *rabbit, umbrella, villain, cottage, muddy* and many others.

When the vowel sound is LONG, or when there are TWO vowels together, the consonant is NOT usually doubled:—

*raining* (two vowels, so one N); *paler* (the A makes an AI sound, so there is only one L); *tiny* (one N, because of the long I sound; with a short I sound you get *tinny*!). Look at these examples as well:— *tulip, basin, final, holy* (notice the difference from *holly*!).

This rule works very well when you are adding ED or ING to words that end in a single consonant. Double the consonant if there is a SINGLE SHORT VOWEL:—

*pat — patting; sit — sitting; pad — padded;* and for other endings too: *sad — sadder.*

But unfortunately things are not as simple as this. For longer words the rule has an extra part:—

DOUBLE the consonant after a SHORT VOWEL, ONLY if the short vowel is STRESSED. The part of the word you 'stress', is the part you say most clearly. In *skittle*, it is the *skitt* part, not the *le* part; in *bullet* it is the *bull* part not the *et* part! Practise with some words yourself, to see which sound or syllable is stressed.

There is ONE additional complication! Words ending in L change to LL wherever the stress falls:— *travelling, tunnelling, modelling.*

Before the Wordlist though, there are some other little notes about endings:—

(i)     IE words change the IE to Y when adding ING (*die — dying*).

(ii)    Y words change to IE when you want to add ED or ER (*cry — cried; fly — flier*).

(iii)   When you are putting an ending on words that end in a slient E, simply remove the E, and put the ending on; do not double anything! (*make — making*).

(iv)   The exception to (iii)! The E stays in a very few words where it is needed to avoid confusion: *dyeing* and *singeing*, which are not the same as *dying* and *singing*.

## WORDLIST (1) — Some Double Consonants

| | | | | | | |
|---|---|---|---|---|---|---|
| mitten | attend | attack | Scottish | pattern | sudden | sullen |
| collar | villain | swallow | shilling | gallop | ballot | challenge |
| carrot | correct | quarry | horrid | summit | errand | happen |
| appeal | traffic | essay | stubborn | village | ribbon | button |
| happy | penny | silly | sorry | yellow | marry | borrow |

## WORDLIST (2) — Some Odd Single Consonants (You would expect them to be double!)

| | | | | | | |
|---|---|---|---|---|---|---|
| habit | cabin | rapid | satin | damage | madam | vinegar |
| Briton | Britain | British | prison | pity | city | finish |
| linen | spirit | limit | timid | lily | widow | lemon |
| enemy | skeleton | remedy | copy | modest | modern | robin |
| punish | study | sugar | Japan | seven | river | shiver |

## WORDLIST (3) — Stress and Verb Endings (With one or two nouns and adjectives as well!)

| | | | | | |
|---|---|---|---|---|---|
| scatter | — scáttering | | | profit | — prófited |
| differ | — dífferent | | | audit | — aúdited |
| offer | — óffered | | refer | — reférred | market | — márketing |
| proffer | — próffering | | — réference (!) | deposit | — depósition |
| mutter | — múttered | prefer | — preférring | solicit | — solícitor |
| order | — órdering | | — préference (!) | spirit | — spírited |
| consider | — consíderation | deter | — detérrent | edit | — éditing |
| remember | — remémbered | expel | — expélling | admit | — admítted |
| render | — réndering | propel | — propélled | submit | — submítted |
| shelter | — shéltered | travel | — trávelling (!) | remit | — remítting |
| snigger | — sníggering | model | — módelling (!) | | |
| | | pardon | — párdoning | | |
| | | flatten | — fláttened | | |

*Note:* The accent ( ´ ) shows where the stress falls.

## EXERCISES

a)  All the following words obey these two rules:—
SHORT SINGLE VOWELS are followed by a DOUBLE consonant.
LONG VOWELS or PAIRS of VOWELS are followed by a SINGLE consonant.
Write out the *correct* spelling *only* for each pair.

| | | | | |
|---|---|---|---|---|
| vila | miser | babby | alow | solo |
| villa | misser | baby | allow | sollo |
| lilac | fuler | shinny | beggin | happen |
| lillac | fuller | shiny | begin | hapen |
| minow | sory | local | courage | anual |
| minnow | sorry | loccal | courrage | annual |
| naval | difference | dilema | unnicorn | gossip |
| navval | diference | dilemma | unicorn | gosip (20) |

b)  The difference between the words in the following pairs is simply double letter or single letter.
Write the pairs out, and next to each word write what it *means*.

| | | | | |
|---|---|---|---|---|
| dinner | canning | ragged | comma | furry |
| diner | caning | raged | coma | fury |
| filling | hallo | bellow | pinned | marry |
| filing | halo | below | pined | Mary (10) |

c)  Here are some verbs which are *not* in the third Wordlist opposite. However, the same rule applies to them. Your task is to write next to each its present participle and past participle. (That is no problem: the present participle is the one ending in ING, the past participle the one ending in ED.)
SAY the word to yourself to find where the STRESS falls, and then obey the rule you have been given on the Factsheet.

| | | | | |
|---|---|---|---|---|
| gallop | infer | regret | open | label |
| repel | compel | bother | murmur | allot |
| commit | acquit | sharpen | develop | defer |

iron (the verb *to iron* — as in clothes . . .)

For the next four words, only write the present participle (-ING). There is a bonus mark for guessing WHY.

| | | | |
|---|---|---|---|
| sit | begin | put | forget |

For the next two words write *both* participles again, — but think carefully about them:—

permit (the verb, *to permit*, not the noun, a *permit*).
rebel (the verb, *to rebel*, not the noun, a *rebel*).

Award yourself another bonus mark if you can explain WHY the difference between these words as nouns and as verbs is important here. (20)

## SPELLING TESTS

| 1 | 2 | 3 | 4 | 5 |
|---|---|---|---|---|
| carrot | settle | kitten | stubborn | dying |
| adder | raining | tiny | bottom | dyeing |
| baler | horrid | tinny | holly | sadder |
| summit | damage | widow | holy | sudden |
| rapid | copy | pity | lily | study |
| deterred | expelled | skeleton | preference | lemon |
| deterrent | dispelling | referring | preferred | propelling |
| different | scattered | modelled | travelling | pardoned |
| differing | auditing | offering | spirited | mattering |
| marketed | admitted | considering | remembering | profiting |

When you are learning longer words, always break them up into their separate sounds or syllables. Also when there IS a rule (like the rule about which part is stressed for doubling or not doubling consonants), try to memorize that as well.

# FACTSHEET SIXTEEN

This Factsheet is concerned with the thing we most commonly add to words — the letter S. We do this to make the PLURAL of words (i.e. when we are talking about more than one thing), and most of the rules that follow are concerned with plurals, those with S and the others!

We also add S to make the *third person singular* of verbs (as in: *he talks, she runs, it barks*), and some notes about verbs are therefore also included.

There is no separate wordlist; the examples are all included under the separate headings.

RULE (1)   Most nouns make their plural by adding S: *dogs, houses, ties, combs, pictures, buildings.*

RULE (2)   Nouns that end in Y change the Y to I and add ES:—
*lady — ladies; fly — flies; daisy — daisies; battery — batteries; diary — diaries; activities, anniversaries, injuries, comedies, arteries* — and many others.
(When you want to add an S to verbs ending in Y, the same rule applies:—
*to fly — he flies; apply — applies; deny — denies; vary — varies* — and many others.)

RULE (3)   is an exception to Rule (2).
When the word ends in AY, EY, OY, UY, simply add S. Do NOT change the Y to I!
*valley — valleys; runway — runways; guy — guys; monkey — monkeys; boy — boys.*
(The same applies to verbs:— *repay — repays; destroy — destroys; convey — conveys.*)

RULE (4)   When a noun ends in S, SS, SH, CH or X — add ES to form the plural:—
*glass — glasses; dish — dishes; church — churches; box — boxes; gas — gases; addresses, successes, mattresses; circuses, crocuses; splashes, parishes.*
(Once again, verbs are much the same:— *detach — detaches; relax — relaxes; refresh — refreshes; assess — assesses; surpass — surpasses.*)

RULE (5)   Some nouns ending in F change the F to V and add ES.
A few nouns ending in FE also change the F to V, and then add S.
*loaf — loaves; wolf — wolves; shelf — shelves; thief — thieves; leaf — leaves; life — lives; knife — knives; wife — wives.*

RULE (6)   is the exception to Rule (5).
Some nouns in F or FE simply add S:—
*gulfs, roofs, chiefs, fifes, proofs, griefs, beliefs.*
Some nouns can have either FS or VES:— *scarfs/scarves; dwarfs/dwarves; hoofs/hooves.*
Verbs do NOT change F to V, as in: He *loafs* about the house; She *leafs* through the book.

RULE (7)   Nouns ending in a vowel plus O (EO, IO, OO) simply add S:— *ratios, studios, oratorios, radios, cameos, boos, folios, cuckoos, kangaroos, cockatoos, stereos, videos.*

RULE (8)   Most other nouns ending in O add ES:— *heroes, cargoes, echoes, potatoes, tomatoes, mosquitoes, tornadoes, torpedoes, zeroes.*
(NB: do not make the mistake of putting an E on any of these words in the singular!)

RULE (9)   is the exception to Rule (8).
There are some other O words that simply add S:— *pianos, tangos, solos, photos, commandos, embryos* (because the Y acts like I) and *twos.* (Yes it can have a plural!)
And quite a few words make their plural in either OS or OES:— *grottos/grottoes, mottos/mottoes, stilettos/stilettoes, volcanos/volcanoes, banjos/banjoes, halos/haloes.*

RULE (10)  Some nouns change their form in the plural:— *man — men, woman — women, child — children; mouse — mice, goose — geese, ox — oxen; tooth — teeth, foot — feet.*

RULE (11)  Some nouns have the same singular and plural (i.e. they do not change):— *sheep, deer, salmon, cannon, grouse.*

RULE (12)  Some nouns have two plural forms, depending on the use or meaning:—
*penny — pence/pennies; shot — shot/shots; index — indexes/indices; genius — genii* (spirits) and *geniuses* (clever people).

RULE (13)  Some words have no singular:— *trousers, shorts* (meaning 'trousers'); *scissors; spectacles, glasses* (meaning 'spectacles'); *victuals* (pronounced 'vittles') and *cattle.*

RULE (14)  Nouns made up of several words only make the MAIN word plural:—
*brothers-in-law,* NOT 'brother-in-laws'; *men of war* (= warships); *passers-by; courts martial,* NOT 'court martials'; *bye-laws.*

RULE (15)  Some words that come from foreign languages have kept foreign plurals:—
*terminus — termini, fungus — fungi; memorandum — memoranda, automaton — automata; axis — axes, basis — bases, crisis — crises, oasis — oases; plateau — plateaux, bureau — bureaux.*

# EXERCISES

(a) Choose the correct form of the plural from the alternatives you are given:—

    (1)   piano — pianoes, pianos

    (2)   radio — radioes, radios

    (3)   wife — wifes, wives

    (4)   belief — beliefs, believes

    (5)   turkey — turkies, turkeys

    (6)   family — famileys, families, familys

    (7)   crisis — crises, crisises, criseses

    (8)   circus — circusses, circes, circuses

    (9)   goose — gooses, geeses, geese, gice

    (10)  ladys-in-waiting — ladies-in-waitings, lady-in-waitings, ladies-in-waiting    (10)

(b) Give the *singular* form of each of the following words:—

| mice | salmon | oxen | thieves | cries |
|------|--------|------|---------|-------|
| salaries | mattresses | potatoes | indices | termini (5) |

(c) Write out the following sentences, inserting the *plural* forms of the nouns given in brackets, and the correct (*third person singular, present tense*) forms of the verbs.

    (1)   He (display) his (injury) to the other (child).

    (2)   She (relax) on the sofa, and idly (leaf) through the (page) of a book.

    (3)   The (echo) of distant (shot) disturb the silence of the (church).

    (4)   (Monkey) chatter in the (tree) above the thatched (roof), while in the village streets beneath (mosquito) hum their tuneless song.

    (5)   A gang of (thief) recently stole the entire (content) of the (shelf) in a local sweet shop; police are looking for people with badly decayed (tooth).

    (6)   Above the wide (plateau) two grim (volcano) reared their shrouded heads toward the distant (sky).    (10)

(d) In this exercise you are given some pieces of nonsense rhymes. The nonsense is made even worse by the poor spelling of most of the plurals and some of the S-forms of verbs. Rewrite them, correcting the mistakes. (You should find twenty in the whole exercise.)

    (1)   He washs the dishs with crashs and splashs.

    (2)   She plaies two pianoes, and soloes on banjose,
           She frequently usess her tooths or her feets.

    (3)   There were mouses dancing tangoes with reckless abandon
           And the hoofes of the cuckooes made noisis like cannons.

    (4)   They sent memorandas to distant oasises
           And letters quite full of disgraceful grimaceses.    (10)

(e) Give the plural of all of the words in this list. They are not mentioned on the Factsheet, but by checking the rules, and using your dictionary, you should be able to work them out.

| gas | scratch | jockey | pigmy | thrush | reply | punch | bluff |
|-----|---------|--------|-------|--------|-------|-------|-------|
| alloy | couch | torch | reproof | brooch | cough | hoe | sheaf |
| reef | wretch | staff | latch | paradox | chateau | service | radish |
| sheriff | research | giraffe | albatross | innuendo | himself (*Be careful, this one is a trick.*) | | (15) |

# SPELLING TESTS

| 1 | 2 | 3 | 4 | 5 |
|---|---|---|---|---|
| daisy | battery | diary | injury | vary |
| daisies | batteries | diaries | injuries | varies |
| valleys | monkeys | runways | repays | destroys |
| mattresses | circus | splashes | gas | parishes |
| wolves | circuses | thieves | gases | assess |
| chiefs | shelves | beliefs | lives | assesses |
| cargoes | heroes | potatoes | tomatoes | mosquitoes |
| radios | studios | pianos | solos | trousers |
| scissors | spectacles | crisis | plateau | victuals |
| mothers-in-law | courts-martial | crises | plateaux | bye-laws |

Some of the most common spelling mistakes involve the use of the apostrophe. It in fact has two main uses.

(1) In shortened forms of words apostrophes are used to show that a letter or letters have been missed out.

This is most common between a personal pronoun (I, you, he, she, it, we, they) and its verb (e.g. *I'm, you've, he's, she'll, it's, we'd, they're*); and in forming negatives (the 'not' forms) of verbs (e.g. *aren't, can't, haven't, won't*).

There are also combinations with 'that' (*that's*), 'there' (*there's*) and 'who' (*who's*).

There are also some shortened words which have apostrophes. The most common of these is *o'clock*, which means 'of the clock'.

You can also use apostrophes to join nouns to verbs:— *Sandra's* (i.e. 'Sandra is') *coming; The postman's been* (i.e. 'has been'). On the whole it is best only to do this when it is easy to pronounce the result. (*Fred'd seen him* is not good idea, for example.)

The common abbreviations using an apostrophe are included in the Wordlist.

(2) Apostrophes are used to show possession or ownership.
Instead of writing *The dress of the girl* we can write *The girl's dress*.

Suppose we wanted to write *The dresses of the girls* in shortened form. The correct version is: *The girls' dresses*.

Here are some RULES to learn:—

(a) Possession is shown in the singular by putting *apostrophe plus S* after the word.

(b) In plural words, where the plural is formed by adding S already, put an *apostrophe after the S*. (The S of course is already there!)

(c) In plural words that do not end in S (like 'women' and 'geese'), put *apostrophe plus S* after the word — as you would for a singular. (So *women's* means *of the women* or *belonging to more than one woman*!)

(d) In singular words that end in S, put an *apostrophe plus S* in the normal way. (So, *The expansion of the gas* would become *The gas's expansion*. If you wanted to say *The expansion of the gases* it would be *The gases' expansion*.)

(e) When you want to make *names* that end in S into possessives, you can either put an apostrophe after the S or add another apostrophe S. (So, both *St James's church* and *young James' book* are correct.)

(f) NEVER USE APOSTROPHES TO FORM ORDINARY PLURALS.
(So *There are two new girl's in our class* is nonsense, and so is *Apples', oranges' and banana's for sale*.)

Remember, apostrophes stand for possession, or for a letter missed out — ONLY.


## WORDLIST

I'm (*I am*)    I'd (*I had, I should, I would*)    I've (*I have*)    I'll (*I shall, I will*)

You're (*you are*)    you'd (*you had, should, would*)    you've (*you have*)    you'll (*you will*)

He's (*he is, he has*)    he'd (*he would, should, had*)    he'll (*he will*)

She's (*she is, she has*)    she'd (*she would, should, had*)    she'll (*she will*)

It's (*it is, it has*)    (*Try not to use "it'll" and "it'd" — they are very poor English.*)

We're (*we are*)    we'd (*we had, we would, we should*)    we've (*we have*)    we'll (*we shall/will*)

They're (*they are*)    they'd (*they had, would, should*)    they've (*they have*)    they'll (*they will*)

That's (*that is, that has*)    there's (*there is, has*)

Who's (*who is, who has*)    who'd (*who would, should, had*)

Aren't (*are not*)    isn't (*is not*)    hasn't (*has not*)    hadn't (*had not*)    haven't (*have not*)

Didn't (*did not*)    doesn't (*does not*)    don't (*do not*)    won't (*will not*)    shan't (*shall not*)

Can't (*cannot (!)*)    couldn't (*could not*)    wouldn't (*would not*)    shouldn't (*should not*)

O'clock (*of the clock*);    'tis (*it is*)    e'er (*ever*)    e'en (*even*) — all in poetry.

NOTICE    its = of it; it's = it is/it has. *You must learn the difference!*
their = of them (adjective); theirs (no apostrophe) = of them (pronoun);
there = that place; there's = there is/there has; they're = they are;
whose = of whom; no apostrophe — and *not* the same as who's.

## EXERCISES

(a) Write out the following sentences inserting an apostrophe where one is missing:—

    (1) Whos afraid of the big bad wolf?

    (2) I dont know whats the matter with him.

    (3) He insisted hed done it, but we all knew he hadnt.

    (4) I cant see them, its too dark — but I know theyre here somewhere.

    (5) Wont you come in. When youve taken your coat off Ill get you a cup of tea.

    (6) If youve already promised them that youd be there at one oclock youll have to hurry up, wont you?

    (7) Mrs Jonesll want to know whos been in here during break.

    (8) Alisons been round while you were out, but Judy hasnt.        (10)

(b) Now write out the sentences again, *using the full forms of the shortened words instead of the forms with the apostrophes.*    (10)

(c) In this exercise there are *forty* mistakes connected with the presence or absence of apostrophes. Rewrite the sentences, correcting the mistakes. Underline the words you have changed.

    (1) There are three of them, but there not all the same.

    (2) Its obvious that the dog hasent had it's dinner yet, James'.

    (3) Whose supposed to be coming on this trip? I warn you, Im only taking those who's names are on the list.

    (4) Your's are they're, but I can'not see Charleses' — and Henries' book's are missing too.

    (5) There are four books' on the floor; perhaps their the missing one's.

    (6) My friends answer's we're the same as Martin Smiths', but he said he had'nt copied them.

    (7) The childrens' mother wasnt in; shed gone out to collect old clothe's for St Andrews' church jumble sale.

    (8) The cabbages price is far too high, so buy the sprout's instead, — and get me some parsnips' too. — In fact, while I think of it, I'de better have a pound of tomato's and five pound's of potatoes' while youre they're.

    (9) The mices feet's had made tracks across the creams' surface in the cats own bowl.    (20)

(d) Rewrite the following, using apostrophes to show possession.
(For example:— *More than one tongue of more than one serpent* would become *The serpents' tongues.* — Notice how the apostrophe when used correctly can give a great deal of information in a very short form.)

    (1) more than one dress of more than one lady

    (2) more than one foot of one child

    (3) one mother of more than one child

    (4) one ox of one owner

    (5) more than one rein of more than one ox

    (6) one mass of one gas

    (7) more than one mass of more than one gas

    (8) one spire of one church

    (9) more than one crash of more than one lorry

    (10) one cub of one fox    (10)

## SPELLING TESTS

| 1 | 2 | 3 | 4 | 5 |
|---|---|---|---|---|
| I'm | we're | we've | it's | there |
| your | that's | there's | its | their |
| you're | you'd | I'll | aren't | theirs |
| yours | who's | can't | he'd | they're |
| isn't | whose | shan't | won't | there's |
| she's | haven't | child's | mustn't | o'clock |
| church's | mouse's | children's | lady's | dresses |
| churches | mice's | voice's | ladies | dresses' |
| churches' | man's | voices' | ladies' | dress's |
| gases | men's | James's | gas's | gases' |

*When doing the tests, the questions could be given in the "I am" rather than "I'm" form, and the "belonging to more than one man" rather than "men's" form.*

In Factsheet Fifteen we looked at some of the rules about past tenses of verbs — adding ED. Another thing that you have to be careful about in English is verbs that do NOT form their past tense by adding ED.

In fact there are two odd or 'irregular' forms to watch out for:— the *past tense,* and the *past participle.* The past participle follows 'have' and 'had' etc. Look at these examples:— *Forget;* past tense *forgot;* past participle *forgotten. Know;* past tense *knew;* past participle *known.* Quite often the past tense and past participle are the same, but not always. Most of this page, as you can see, is the Wordlist of all these irregular verbs.

## WORDLIST

| Present Tense | Past Tense | Past Participle | Present Tense | Past Tense/Participle | Present Tense | Past Tense/Participle |
|---|---|---|---|---|---|---|
| freeze | froze | frozen | win | won | dig | dug |
| choose | chose | chosen | shine | shone | slink | slunk |
| eat | ate | eaten | hang | hung *or* hanged | spin | spun |
| fly | flew | flown | | | stick | stuck |
| go | went | gone | hold | held | strike | struck |
| do | did | done | sit | sat | string | strung |
| sew | sewed | sewn | slide | slid | swing | swung |
| show | showed | shown | bring | brought | wring | wrung |
| saw | sawed | sawn | buy | bought | bind | bound |
| swell | swelled | swollen | catch | caught | find | found |
| fall | fell | fallen | seek | sought | grind | ground |
| draw | drew | drawn | teach | taught | fight | fought |
| slay | slew | slain | think | thought | bleed | bled |
| blow | blew | blown | burn | burnt | breed | bred |
| grow | grew | grown | creep | crept | feed | fed |
| know | knew | known | deal | dealt | lead | led |
| throw | threw | thrown | dream | dreamt *or* dreamed | read | read (sound but not spelling "red") |
| begin | began | begun | | | | |
| drink | drank | drunk | dwell | dwelt | speed | sped (though 'speeded' also exists) |
| give | gave | given | feel | felt | | |
| lie | lay | lain (to rest) | kneel | knelt | hear | heard |
| lie | lied | lied (to fib) | lean | leant *or* leaned | build | built (though 'builded' also exists) |
| ring | rang | rung | | | | |
| shrink | shrank | shrunk | leap | leapt *or* leaped | meet | met |
| sing | sang | sung | | | light | lit |
| sink | sank | sunk | leave | left | bend | bent |
| spring | sprang | sprung | lose | lost | rend | rent |
| swim | swam | swum | mean | meant | send | sent |
| run | ran | run | sleep | slept | spend | spent |
| break | broke | broken | spell | spelt *or* spelled | | |
| bear | bore | born or borne* | | | | |
| speak | spoke | spoken | spill | spilt | | |
| steal | stole | stolen | sweep | swept | | |
| tear | tore | torn | weep | wept | | |
| wear | wore | worn | flee | fled | | |
| weave | wove | woven | have | had | | |
| bite | bit | bitten | lay | laid | | |
| give | gave | given | make | made | | |
| beat | beat | beaten | pay | paid | | |
| shake | shook | shaken | say | said | | |
| forsake | forsook | forsaken | sell | sold | | |
| take | took | taken | shoe | shod | | |
| drive | drove | driven | tell | told | | |
| ride | rode | ridden | get | got | | |
| rise | rose | risen | spit | spat | | |
| arise | arose | arisen | fling | flung | | |
| strive | strove | striven | cling | clung | | |
| write | wrote | written | sling | slung | | |
| hide | hid | hidden | hold | held | | |
| wake | woke | woken *or* wakened | behold | beheld | | |
| tread | trod | trodden *or* trod | stand | stood | | |
| come | came | come | | | | |

The following words are THE SAME in the present tense, past tense, and past participle:—

| | |
|---|---|
| spread | put |
| cast | set |
| cost | shut |
| cut | slit |
| hit | split |
| hurt | thrust |
| rid | wet (though 'wetted' |
| burst | also exists). |

*NB *borne* is an (old-fashioned) word meaning 'carried'; *born* always refers to babies!

# EXERCISES

a) Rewrite the following brief 'story in sentences', putting the verbs into the *past tense*.

(1)  A boy steals an apple from the shop.
(2)  The owner goes for the police.
(3)  A policeman pursues the boy.
(4)  He blows his whistle.
(5)  A crowd begins to form.
(6)  They get in the way of the policeman.
(7)  He fights his way through.
(8)  However, he loses sight of the boy.
(9)  He surveys the scene hopelessly.
(10)  The boy hides round a corner.  (10)

b) This exercise is the exact reverse. Rewrite the 'story in sentences', changing it from the past to the present tense.

(1)  Its rider leant low on its back as the horse galloped on through the night.
(2)  Few saw their passage as onward they sped over hill and valley.
(3)  They burst through the hedges, leapt over the walls, and cut through the woodlands.
(4)  They sprang across trickling streams; they swam a wide river.
(5)  Only the moon lit their way.  (10)

c) Insert a suitable form of a verb into the spaces in the following sentences. You are given the present tenses of the verbs to choose from at the end of the exercise.

(1)  Have you ............ our anniversary again?
(2)  I ............ I saw a pussy cat.
(3)  Too late! I see the birds have ............ .
(4)  After they had ............ they always ............ hands.
(5)  What did you ............ Veronica for her birthday?
(6)  But doesn't she already ............ a set or ornamental foot-scrapers?
(7)  How many times have I ............ you about tidying your room?
(8)  What a mess you have ............ in the kitchen!
(9)  Which of you children has ............ this cement mixer?

(have    shake    think    tell    make    forget    fight    break    fly    give)  (10)

d) Here is part of a pleasant little ghost story, but no less than twenty verbs in the past tense have been spelt wrong or given the wrong form. Write it out again, correcting the words that are wrong. Underline each word you have changed:—

I lighted the candles, but their flames at once growed dim in the chill air of the great hall of that ancient castle.

"The bones of old Sir Hugh have lied here long," sayed Doomley, the butler, "but now his ghost has rised, and we have all sawed his eerie form, walking to and fro upon the battlements."

When Doomley had at last went, I sitted down on the cold stone floor, and eated some of my food — after I had heaten it up on my primus stove of course. I also drunk a little of my whisky, and fealt a good bit better. Then, suddenly, I heared a hideous, groaning voice, right behind me. In a moment the air become deathly cold.

"I have came for you, Sanders," cryed the ghost with a cackling laugh.

I spinned round, and before my eyes I beholded a ghastly shape. I standed there, freezed to the spot, unable to move a muscle. What would be my terrible fate . . .?  (20)

# SPELLING TESTS

| 1 | 2 | 3 | 4 | 5 |
|---|---|---|---|---|
| swell | fight | strike | teach | awaken |
| swollen | fought | struck | taught | awoke |
| hide | leap | buy | ate | awoken |
| hid | leapt | bought | eaten | wakened |
| hidden | choose | steal | beat | bite |
| read (pres.) | chose | stole | beaten | bitten |
| read (past) | chosen | stolen | leave | build |
| lead | threw | write | left | built |
| led | thrown | wrote | kneel | grind |
| arisen | drawn | written | knelt | ground |

We have already had a look at C, K and CK as endings on Factsheet Fourteen. The Wordlist on this page includes some more words that end in C, rather than CK, together with words ending in CT.

But C can be much more of a problem in words than just in their endings.

K and CK, as you would expect, always make a K sound:— *pocket, stockings, chicken, packet; kettle, keeper, kipper, kitchen, kangaroo.*

When it comes IN FRONT OF the vowels A, O and U, and also in front of any consonant, C also makes the K SOUND:— *capture, calculate, candle, capital, coffee, colour, combat, culture, customer, cushion.*

But IN FRONT OF E, I and Y, C makes an S SOUND:— *cell, cease, certain, centre, circle, city, cinema, cycle, cymbal, cylinder.*

The same rule applies to the letter G. In front of A, O and U, the letter G makes a G sound:— *gamble, govern, guardian.*

In front of E, I and Y, the letter G makes a J sound:— *general, gigantic, gypsy.*

But there are exceptions:— *gift, gild, gird, girder, girdle, girl, give, get.*

Because of the similarity in these rules, G words are included here as well.

You will also find on the Wordlist, several words where C occurs in some strange spellings. There is also a group of words where the K sound is spelt CH.

## WORDLIST

| More words ending in the letters IC | Some words ending in the letters CT | CE CI and CY | CH spelling K |
|---|---|---|---|
| music | attract | parcel | school |
| public | contact | central | scholar |
| arithmetic | compact | cities | scheme |
| Arctic | abstract | cigar | Christ |
| Antarctic | extract | cigarette | Christmas (remember the T!) |
| Pacific | impact | sincere | Christian |
| Atlantic | react | recite | chorus |
| domestic | subtract | saucer | ache |
| athletic | transact | December | headache |
| electric | | concern | character |
| heroic | affect* | precinct | stomach |
| Catholic | effect* | princess | echo |
| republic | | recent | |
| metric | collect | fancy | SOME PROBLEM WORDS |
| cosmic | correct | mercy | |
| tropics | direct | certificate | disciple (silent C) |
| politics | detect | necessary (SS) | discipline (silent C) |
| italics | elect | associate (SS) | |
| mathematics | expect | conceal | concert (C sounds like S) |
| | infect | magnificent | concerto (C sounds like CH) |
| musical | project | ceremony | |
| electrical | subject | docile | succeed (CC sounds like CS) |
| tropical | respect | | success (CC sounds like CS) |
| political | | | accept (CC sounds like CS) |
| mathematical | concoct | GE GI and GY | accident (CC sounds like CS) |
| | deduct | | |
| republican | instruct | gem | schism (silent CH: 'sism') |
| | obstruct | magic | |
| *Remember that* | viaduct | German | occur (CC sounds like K) |
| *the shorter words* | aqueduct | Germany | accompany (CC sounds like K) |
| *nearly always end* | | Belgium | accomplish (CC sounds like K) |
| *in ICK, not IC* | *Do not confuse* | Belgian | according (CC sounds like K) |
| | *these words with* | region | |
| | *past tenses ending in* | gentle | occupy (CC sounds like K) |
| | *ED, like:—* | genuine | |
| | | digest | ocean (CE sounds like SH!) |
| | smacked | origin | |
| | wrecked | imagine | margarine (GA sounds like JA!) |
| | shocked | giant | |
| | ducked | gymnasium | suggest (GG sounds like J) |

*Note: Use your dictionary to try and find out the difference in meaning between these two very similar words.*

## EXERCISES

(a) In the following sentences some words from the Wordlist have been spelt (or, in one case, *used*) incorrectly. Write out the sentences putting right what is wrong.
   (1) Boys will acsept firm dissipline, so long as it is fair.
   (2) Can you direcked me to the Belgium frontier, please?
   (3) The prinsess is to open the new shopping presinct tomorrow.
   (4) If you do that again you can eckspecked to be smact.
   (5) If your repentance is sinsere, I may yet show you mersy.
   (6) You, sir, are a scolar, a jentleman, and a fine judge of horseflesh.
   (7) Nothing suckseeds like sucsess.
   (8) The seremony concluded with a magnifisent musickal finale.
   (9) I have never found it difficult to tell margearine from butter.
   (10) The inhabitants of Jermany are called Germs.                          (20)

(b) In this exercise, your task is to choose the correct spelling from the alternatives given in the brackets.
   (1) I have never enjoyed (abstrackt, abstract, abstracked) painting.
   (2) The canal will cross the valley on an (aqueducked, aqueduct, aqueduckt).
   (3) (Scool, shcool, school) always gives me a (headacke, headache, headake).
   (4) The (resent, rescent, recent) (sceme, skeme, scheme) to establish new (sentral, kentral, central) and (regional, rejonal, regonal) offices was (origionally, orijinally, originally) (rejected, regected, rejeckted) by the board of the company.                          (10)

(c) The following words are *not* in the Wordlist. You have to choose the correct spelling once again. You will need to use your dictionary.
Look at the correct spellings to see how they fit in with what you have learnt.

| | | | | |
|---|---|---|---|---|
| tragedy | deception | genial | acsent | exsellent |
| trajedy | deseption | jenial | accent | excellent |
| | | | | |
| regect | monarky | biolojy | execute | prophetic |
| reject | monarchy | biology | execkute | prophetick |

(10)

(d) An important part of spelling is learning the meanings that go with the words. Find in the Wordlist, or elsewhere on the Factsheet, the words that go with these meanings:—
   (1) A round tube, often part of an engine and containing a piston.
   (2) To go somewhere with someone; or to play music to support a singer.
   (3) Truly meant or felt; honest and genuine.
   (4) A long bridge, often with many arches, that carries a road or railway.
   (5) Something that happens by chance or unexpectedly; often a misfortune.
   (6) To work something out, often by maths.
   (7) To say aloud something that you have learnt by heart.
   (8) A fight or contest; fighting.
   (9) A follower; particularly one of the followers of Jesus.
   (10) To hide.                          (10)

## SPELLING TESTS

| 1 | 2 | 3 | 4 | 5 |
|---|---|---|---|---|
| Pacific | Arctic | heroic | mathematics | electrical |
| react | instruct | elect | subtract | shocked |
| central | cities | recent | fancy | saucer |
| pocket | cigarette | cinema | cycle | giant |
| cushion | necessary | kitchen | magic | gigantic |
| character | headache | genuine | magnificent | girder |
| origin | ceremony | certificate | concern | accept |
| disciple | Christian | Belgium | scholar | stomach |
| occur | schism | accident | success | discipline |
| ocean | margarine | suggest | occupy | according |

Remember to keep up your own list of words that *you* find difficult. Those are the ones you need to concentrate on, and to test yourself on. Try to give yourself your own 'clue words' or reminders, like those in the earlier Wordlists, or those given for the 'problem words' opposite.

Having seen some problems with consonants, particularly C, we will now look at some problem combinations of vowels. First is:— IE or EI.

In shorter words IE often makes a LONG I sound (as in *tie*, *cried* etc.). But it can also make an EE sound (as in *thief*), an E sound (as in *friendship*), and the sound in *alien* (ay-lee-en)! EI tends to make an AY sound (as in *reign*, *eight*, *neigh*).

In longer words there is a general rule about EI and IE:—

> "I before E, except after C,
> Can only be when it rhymes with me."

The second line of this rhyme is as important as the first. If you look in the Wordlist you will see several words where IE follows C, but it does not make an EE sound, so it is not breaking the rule.

Let us sum up this awkward sound:—

IE sometimes spells a LONG I sound, especially in shorter words (like *lie*, *dies*).

IE can also spell an EE sound (*believe*, *relief*, *cashier*) but NOT AFTER C.

EI often spells an AY sound (*neighbour*, *reindeer*, *eighty*).

EI can also spell an EE sound, in a few short words (*seize*, *seizure*, *weird*), and in long words DIRECTLY AFTER C (*receive*, *ceiling*).

There are also of course other odd words, where IE and EI spell all sorts of sounds, as you will see in the following Wordlist.

## WORDLIST (1)

**IE = LONG I SOUND**
defied
supplied
replies
unties
*and many others.*

**IE =EE SOUND**
achieve
retrieve
belief
believe
relief
handkerchief
besiege
fiercely
*and also many plurals:—*
ladies, babies, diaries (books) and dairies (milk)!

**EI = AY SOUND**
weigh
weight
eighteen
neighbourhood

**EI = OTHER SOUNDS**
heifer
counterfeit
forfeit
leisure
sovereign
foreign
foreigner
eiderdown
seize (EE sound)

**EI AFTER C**
receive
receipt
deceive
deceit
perceive
conceive
conceit

ceiling      (roof)
sealing      (closing)
concealing

*Also notice:—*
deception
conception
reception
perception

**IE AFTER C (!)**
proficient
proficiency
sufficient
deficient
efficient
efficiency
conscience
ancient

science
scientific

ALL WITH A
'SH' SOUND —
and none
rhyming
with ME!

(Silent C)

*Also notice the SH sound in:—*
suspicion      official
patient         patience
special         artificial
social          musician
gracious        precious

## UA OR AU

The second part of this Factsheet also deals with a combination of two vowels that is supposed to be difficult: AU and UA.

In fact there is no great problem. The normal spelling is AU, and it usually (though not always) makes the same sound as AW:— words like *caught*, *cause*, *autumn*, *author*.

UA appears when the U is following a Q (since Q is always followed by a U) or sometimes after a G (when the U is silent). There are also some words where the U and the following A are clearly heard separate sounds, and when the U is acting like a W.

## WORDLIST (2)

**UA after Q**
quarry
equation
quantity
qualify
quarrel
squadron
acquaint
equality

**UA after G**
guard
coastguard
guardian
guarantee

**UA (U = W)**
persuade
language

**U + A SEPARATE**
January
February (R!)
gradual
usual
manual
estuary
valuable
situation

**A SELECTION OF AU WORDS**

| | | |
|---|---|---|
| applause | haulage | authority |
| auction | auburn | somersault |
| laundry | audit | audacious |
| naughty | undaunted | automatic |
| cauldron | exhaust | astronaut |
| slaughter | assault | cosmonaut |
| daughter | overhaul | gauntlet |

## EXERCISES

a) This is one of the exercises where you are given a choice of spellings for particular words, and you have to pick the correct one. When you write out the sentences underline the words which you have selected.

(1) If you are (pashent, pacient, patient) you will (receive, recieve, reseave) your just reward.

(2) He (conceiled, concieled, concealed) the documents about his person, but his (deseit, deceit, deciet) was soon discovered.

(3) The (counterfeit, counterfiet, counterfeet) notes failed to (decieve, deceave, deceive) the (officials, offisials, offishials).

(4) Pay the (musitians, musisians, musicians) (eiteen, eihgteen, eighteen) gold (soverans, soveriens, sovereigns), master chamberlain.

(5) We shall have to put up a false (sealing, ceiling, cealing) in the kitchen.

(6) I (believe, beleive, belief) you have dropped your (handkercheif, handkerchiefe, handkerchief), my lady.

(7) The (situation, sitaution, situaution) is (gradually, gradaully, gradualy) improving.

(8) We are still celebrating the (relieve, relief, releif) of Mafeking.

(9) The wicked king cut his old and ugly (duaghter, dauhgter, daughter) into small (peaces, peices, pieces), and put her into a (cauldron, cawldron, cualdron), hoping to make her younger and more beautiful.

(10) Then be boiled her (feircely, fearcely, fiercely) in the pot for (eigthy, eithgy, eighty) days, but she came out just as old and plain as ever.

(11) (Janruary, January, Janaury) is not (usually, usauly, usaully) as cold as (Febraury, February, Febaury).

(12) The (coastguard, coastgaurd, coastgard) helicopter was hovering above the (estruary, estaury, estuary).

(13) A herd of (heffers, hieffers, heifers) was grazing in the (field, feild, feald).

(14) She has learnt to use her (artificial, artificail, artifiscial) limb perfectly.

(15) (Consience, concience, conscience) forbids such frightful acts.

(30)

(b) In the following passage twenty words are spelt wrong. Write out the passage correcting the mistakes. Underline the words you have corrected.

Irina breathed a sigh of releaf. She eased herself into the navigator's chair. With a proficeincy born of long experience she began to aquaint herself with the array of manaul controls. Irina was the cosmonuat entrusted with the recovery mission of the unidentified freighter.

All the writing was in a foriegn langauge of course — an alein alphabet she had never seen before. She percieved that the layout was familiar though. In fact it was not very different from that of the vessels in her own sqaudron. After all, she thought, the sientific principles could not vary; the same eqations had to apply. The ship was on aughtomatic pilot at the moment, and the systems seemed effishient enough. Pateintly she checked the mysterious dials, then, hoping for the best, treid a switch. The radio crackled into life.

"Are you recieving me . . .? Come in, please . . . Have you acheived control of abandoned vessel?" came the distant voice across the void of space.

Reseption was poor, but just sufficeint.

(20)

## SPELLING TESTS

| 1 | 2 | 3 | 4 | 5 |
|---|---|---|---|---|
| cried | guarantee | friendship | persuade | language |
| mischief | usual | believe | relief | cashier |
| guardian | fiercely | handkerchief | valuable | counterfeit |
| eighty | auction | foreigner | naughty | equality |
| leisure | ancient | conscience | science | sufficient |
| receive | receipt | deceive | deceit | perceive |
| February | conceive | coastguard | efficient | reception |
| qualify | conceit | estuary | efficiency | alien |
| exhaust | suspicion | special | musician | patience |
| deficient | somersault | laundry | automatic | slaughter |

On this page we are dealing with silent letters, and the rather similar 'oddities' PH and GH. We have already covered many of these words in the first part of the book, but here they are brought together.

SILENT H   We are calling the H after a W silent. Though many people pronounce it, most now do not, as in common words like: *when, whenever; wheel, wheelchair; whirl, whirlwind.*
It is also found following R (in words like *rhyme*), and at the beginning of some words (such as *honest*).

SILENT W   The silent W usually appears in front of R (*write, written; wreck, wreckage*), but it is also there in *whole, wholly* and *sword.*

SILENT K and SILENT G   These usually turn up in front of the letter N:— *knock* and *knocker, knit* and *knitting; sign* and *signpost, foreigner* and *sovereign.*

SILENT B   is sometimes found after M, as in *climb* and *climber, plumb* (= lead weight) and *plumber.*

There are very many others, as you will see from the Wordlist.

Rather similar are the odd GH words. Most of them are short words, so you should already know them, but there are a few more to add. Even so these are usually combinations formed from these same short words. Remember that GH may have no sound at all, as in *throughout* and *highway,* or an F sound, as in *enough* and *laughter.*

There is also the combination PH. Most words that start with or contain PH — and the RH combination — are from Greek! PH nearly always makes an F sound:— *photograph, physics, phlegm* (with a silent G as well). There are some other Greek words with a silent P that you should be prepared for:— *psalm, psychology* etc.

## WORDLIST

(Not all the words with a silent letter that we have already covered have been included.)

| WH WORDS | WR WORDS | KN WORDS | PH WORDS | GH WORDS | OTHER SILENT LETTERS:— |
|---|---|---|---|---|---|
| wheelbarrow | wrapper | knitting | phase | thorough | C |
| whether | wretched | knapsack | phrase | borough | scenery |
| whichever | wriggle | knuckle | physicist | throughout | muscle |
| whining | wringer | knocker | physician | highway | science |
| whinny | wrinkle | knee | physical | | scented |
| whirlpool | wrangle | knee-cap | | enough | scissors |
| whisker | writing | knot | triumph | laughing | |
| whisper | awry | knotty | graph | | CH |
| whimper | wreckage | | photograph | ghost | yacht |
| whitewash | | GN WORDS | paragraph | ghastly | |
| Whitsun | OTHER SILENT W WORDS | reign | telegraph | ghoulish | D |
| | whole | foreign | autograph | | handsome |
| OTHER SILENT H WORDS | wholly | sovereign | elephant | GHT WORDS | handkerchief |
| rheumatism | wholesome | resign | orphan | daughter | Wednesday |
| rhinoceros | wholemeal | designer | nephew | haughty | |
| rhinoceroses | | ensign | prophet | slaughter | L |
| rhododendron | sword | consignment | sulphur | frightful | folk |
| rhubarb | answer | signpost | sphere | lightning | yolk |
| rhyme | | gnarled | atmosphere | twilight | salmon |
| rhythm | MB WORDS | campaign | hemisphere | nightmare | |
| rhythmical | bomb | | symphony | nightdress | P |
| | bomber | MN WORDS | telephone | | psalm |
| honest | climb | hymn | microphone | laughter | psychiatrist |
| honesty | climber | damn | alphabet | draughty | receipt |
| honour | tomb | autumn | asphalt | | corps |
| honourable | entomb | column | geography | SILENT T AFTER S | cupboard |
| heiress | plumber | condemn | apostrophe | thistle | pneumonia |
| | plumb-line | | catastrophe | whistle | pneumatic |
| exhaust | combing | chimney (*not silent, but not 'chimley'*) | philosophy | castle | |
| exhibit | thumb-nail | | phenomenon | listen | R, S, T . . . |
| | | | | hasten | February |
| | | | | Christmas | island |

*Also notice:* shepherd (silent H, not an F sound)     knowledge (silent K *and* silent W)
depot and debut (pronounced 'deppoe' and 'daybue') and also ballet
isthmus (which has a *nearly* silent TH)     John (the most mis-spelt name)
boatswain and forecastle, which are pronounced, and sometimes spelt bo'sun and fo'csle
myrrh, pharaoh and pterodactyl — to finish with some really strange ones!

Some of the words on these pages are very hard indeed, and it might well be a good idea to spend extra time on them. Try to learn the words in *groups* (as they are shown on the Wordlist) — and, to tell you yet another time, keep your own record of *your* problem words.

## EXERCISES

a) Choose the correct spelling from the PH or F choices you are given.
(1) My (nephew, nefew) has (phew, few) problems with his schoolwork.
(2) I (confess, conphess) that I am poor at (geografy, geography).
(3) (Unphortunately, unfortunately) her (physical, fysical) condition is growing worse.
(4) The light has (affected, aphected) this (fotograf, photograph, photograf, fotograph).
(5) You could have made the (ephort, effort) to (telephone, telefone).
(6) He is the (official, ophicial) (fysician, physician) to the Queen.
(7) The present budget (dephicit, deficit) could be (catastrophic, catastrofic).
(8) The (symfony, symphony) was reaching its (finale, phinale).
(9) (Phumes, fumes) of (sulfur, sulphur) filled the room.
(10) He (referred, repherred) to the wonders of the new (telegraf, telegraph).    (10)

(b) In the following sentences several GH and GHT words have been spelt wrong. Write out the sentences, underlining the right spellings you have inserted.
(1) She ordered the Hieways Department to begin a thoro cleaning programme threwout the burra.
(2) The friteful slorter continued all across the battlefield from dawn to twilite.
(3) She awoke from her nitemare to the all-too-real sounds of gostely laffter.    (10)

(c) You may well not think much of the following poem, but hidden in it are twenty words with a silent letter. Make a list of them.

> The ensigns of war are borne to no campaign
> The Sovereign's realm enjoys Her peaceful reign;
> All honest folk engage in wholesome toil,
> The oxen till the fertile island soil;
> And gnarled old warriors now their swords resign,
> Lay up their knapsacks, bomb and shell consign
> To other days and honourable disuse,
> While they a quiet autumn sunset choose:
> So knowledge, wealth and commerce multiply,
> And only whining wranglers look awry.    (10)

(d) Here are some more bad spellings to put right. They *mostly* concern silent letters . . .
(1) With a winny of fear the horse was swept away in the wirlpool.
(2) It sounds like a herd of rinoceroses loose in our rodedendrons.
(3) A colum of smoke rose from the chimley.
(4) If you move a mussel, I'll rap your nuckles.
(5) I remember that it was the first Wendesday in Febuary.
(6) Lissen to the wind wisseling in the treetops.
(7) I could not hear my syciatrist speak for the noise of the neumatic drills.
(8) "You may like nitting, Joe, but I prefer sammon fishing," said Ermintrude.
(9) Put the roobarb in the cubboard, will you.
(10) The body of the faraoh was annointed with myrhr.    (20)

## SPELLING TESTS

| 1 | 2 | 3 | 4 | 5 |
|---|---|---|---|---|
| whether | wreckage | wheelchair | whisper | Whitsun |
| wretched | knocker | wholly | honest | February |
| bomber | entomb | autumn | answer | Wednesday |
| knuckle | whirlwind | triumph | government | exhaust |
| physics | thistle | consignment | signpost | gnarled |
| symphony | hasten | alphabet | autograph | condemn |
| thorough | receipt | ghostly | muscle | laughter |
| through | microphone | Christmas | frightful | salmon |
| knowledge | physician | rhythm | scissors | asphalt |
| rhinoceros | rheumatism | psychiatrist | psychology | pneumonia |

After the very difficult words introduced on the last Factsheet, this one will seem fairly easy. It deals with homophones, which (you will remember) are words that sound the same but have different spellings, — together with other words that can easily be confused. The Wordlist should provide all the explanation you need!

## WORDLIST

| | | | | | | | |
|---|---|---|---|---|---|---|---|
| allowed | (permitted) | colonel | (officer) | mantel | (fireplace) | weather | (rain) |
| aloud | (not silent) | kernel | (nut) | mantle | (covering) | whether | (if) |
| altar | (holy table) | conquer | (defeat) | medal | (award) | border | (edge) |
| alter | (change) | conker | (nut) | meddle | (interfere) | boarder | (lodger/pupil) |
| berry | (fruit) | council | (town) | metal | (steel) | lessen | (make less) |
| bury | (dig) | counsel | (advice/lawyer) | mettle | (bravery) | lesson | (learn) |
| bridal | (of a bride) | | | muscle | (body) | licence | (*the noun* — C) |
| bridle | (horse) | currant | (fruit) | mussel | (shellfish) | license | (to license, |
| Briton | (person) | current | (stream) | practice | (*the noun* — C) | | *the verb* — S) |
| Britain | (country) | dual | (double) | practise | (*the verb* — S) | naval | (ships) |
| canvas | (cloth) | duel | (fight) | principal | (chief) | navel | (stomach) |
| canvass | (election) | fisher | (fish) | principle | (belief) | | |
| ceiling | (roof) | fissure | (crack) | profit | (gain) | | |
| sealing | (wax) | gamble | (bet) | prophet | (foresees) | | |
| carat | (diamonds) | gambol | (skip) | stationary | (not moving) | Also remember these:— | |
| carrot | (vegetable) | holy | (sacred) | stationery | (paper) | dyeing | (colour) |
| cellar | (basement/salt) | wholly | (entirely) | succour | (help) | dying | (death) |
| | | manner | (way) | sucker | (from *suck*) | singeing | (burn) |
| seller | (who sells) | manor | (house) | | | singing | (noise) |

The next section of the Wordlist is for words that do not sound *the same*, but do have similar spellings or pronunciation.

| | | | | | | | |
|---|---|---|---|---|---|---|---|
| accept | (take) | angel | (spirit) | collar | (neck) | decent | (honourable) |
| except | (excluding) | angle | (corner) | colour | (red) | descent | (going down) |
| expect | (wait for) | borough | (town) | complement | (amount) | desert | (sand) |
| advice | (*noun* — C) | burrow | (hole) | compliment | (praise) | dessert | (pudding) |
| advise | (*verb* — S) | accent | (speech) | warship | (vessel) | lightening | (getting light) |
| dependant | (*noun*—ANT) | ascent | (going up) | worship | (adore) | lightning | (flash) |
| dependent | (*adj.*—ENT) | personal | (private) | prophecy | (*noun* — C) | liable | (likely to) |
| independent | (*always*—ENT) | personnel | (people) | prophesy | (*verb* — S) | libel | (like slander) |

affect    (to have an effect or result on something — often a bad result — *verb*)
effect    (something that happens as a result; *also* a general impression — *noun*)

The next section is a reminder of pairs of words that have the same spelling, but are entirely different words, with different meanings, and different sounds or pronunciation.

| | | | | | | | |
|---|---|---|---|---|---|---|---|
| tear | (rip) | wound | (injure) | bow | (stoop) | row | (line) |
| tear | (weep) | wound | (from *wind*) | bow | (arrow) | row | (noise) |
| wind | (blow) | live | (alive) | sow | (seed) | refuse | (say no) |
| wind | (to wind; *verb*) | live | (to live) | sow | (pig) | refuse | (rubbish) |

read    (present tense: 'I read it now' — sounds like *reed*)
read    (past tense 'I read it yesterday' — sounds like *red*)

Finally, do not make the mistake of trying to give two different spellings for slightly different things, when in fact they are covered by one word and one spelling:—
promise (a promise *and* to promise)        notice (a notice *and* to notice)

Remember that you have already come across a very large number of homophones among the shorter words. They are always paired together in the Wordlists, so check back over them, and any that you know are problems for you should be added to your own list for special attention.

## EXERCISES

(a) In the following sentences, choose the correct spelling from the words in brackets. Write the sentences out, underlining the word you have chosen.

(1) The boys were playing (conquers, conkers) in the street.

(2) Don't move a (mussel, muscle), Louis; I've got you covered.

(3) I will not be spoken to in that (manor, manner), boy. You must learn to (bridle, bridal) your tongue, or it will be the worse for you.

(4) In ancient times the holly was a (wholly, holy) tree.

(5) Be careful, its (berries, buries) are poisonous.

(6) I am not sure if that noise means the third form is (singing, singeing) — or (dyeing, dying).

(7) The lambs were (gambolling, gambling) in the fields.

(8) She was carried away by a swift (currant, current). (10)

(b) In this exercise, each question contains the two different spellings of a pair of homophones. Insert the correct one in each of the spaces.

(1) ............ your piano now, Tommy. Only ............ makes perfect, you know. (practise, practice)

(2) While I am ............ of this school, we shall continue to abide by the old-fashioned ............ of hard work. (principal, principle)

(3) The ............ tells us that there is no ............ to be had in worldly treasures. (profit, prophet)

(4) ............ will remain strong, only while every individual ............ remains free. (Britain, Briton)

(5) The local ............ has taken the advice of ............ about the legality of its plans to sell the town hall. (counsel, council)

(6) The uproar in Miss Sprightly's ............ does not seem to ............ . (lessen, lesson)

(7) I doubt ............ the present spell of good ............ will continue much longer. (weather, whether)

(8) Speaking ............ is not ............ in this corridor. (aloud, allowed)

(9) The ............-piece above the hearth was richly carved, and the flickering light from the gas-............ threw its figures into bold relief. (mantel, mantle)

(10) The ............ of these black-market goods have their bases in dingy back streets and dilapidated ............ (sellers, cellars) (20)

(c) Here is a piece of typical gobbledygook from an official! But this example contains some spelling mistakes. See if you can find them and put them right.

On the basis of independant advise received, we believe that this burrow is not libel for the cost of the improvements. We must advice you therefore that we have expected this opinion, and that accordingly you can except no further assistance accept in respect of works already begun under license which will not be effected. (10)

(d) For this exercise you may have to search in some of the earlier Factsheets and Wordlists. For each of the following words find a homophone. Then write down both words, and give the *meaning* of each.

| | | | | | |
|---|---|---|---|---|---|
| seen | sent | tide | our | yoke | |
| groan | herd | boy | cue | key | (10) |

## SPELLING TESTS

| 1 | 2 | 3 | 4 | 5 |
|---|---|---|---|---|
| allowed | colonel | weather | council | medal |
| aloud | kernel | whether | counsel | meddle |
| license | currant | duel | practise | principal |
| licence | current | dual | practice | principle |
| manner | prophet | dependent | accept | descent |
| manor | profit | dependant | expect | decent |
| effect | prophesy | independent | except | advise |
| affect | prophecy | Britain | holy | advice |
| angel | metal | muscle | holly | notice |
| angle | conquer | lesson | wholly | promise |

This Factsheet and the following ones are looking at the *endings* of words. We are starting by looking at endings in LE, EL and AL. The problem of course is which of these three alternatives goes on which word. There are no rules about this, except some very general ones:—

Most short, simple common words with these endings have LE.
The ending EL is not particularly common.
Most longer words, especially those formed by adding this ending to another word, have AL.

All that is left is to study the Wordlist!

## WORDLIST (1) LE WORDS

| | | | | | | | | |
|---|---|---|---|---|---|---|---|---|
| humble | single | gentle | idle | noble | simple | purple | pimple | pickle |
| feeble | double | able | stable | marble | candle | sparkle | bundle | prickle |
| rifle | trifle | steeple | couple | table | cradle | handle | pickle | measles |
| uncle | jungle | thimble | title | axle | needle | eagle | trouble | buckle |
| people | treacle | turtle | winkle | tremble | tumble | trample | stumble | couple |
| scramble | fumble | grumble | startle | kindle | mingle | gamble | sprinkle | angle |
| hurtle | twinkle | tingle | tickle | sickle | mangle | circle | steeple | *(corner)* |
| | | | | | | | | |
| meddle | cripple | settle | rattle | scribble | ruffle | fiddle | middle | |
| grapple | apple | wriggle | saddle | struggle | puzzle | paddle | cattle | |
| kettle | bottle | dapple | little | ripple | baffle | waddle | battle | |
| | | | | | | | | |
| wrestle | bristle | castle | rustle | whistle | thistle | trestle | | |
| | | | | | | | | |
| article | example | resemble | icicle | miracle | disciple | triangle | rectangle | |
| vehicle | obstacle | pinnacle | bicycle | spectacles | | | | |

## WORDLIST (2) EL WORDS

| | | | | | | | | |
|---|---|---|---|---|---|---|---|---|
| shovel | parcel | tinsel | scoundrel | lintel | model | panel | label | morsel |
| trowel | vowel | towel | chisel | laurel | gospel | chapel | rebel | angel |
| mongrel | camel | jewel | novel | marvel | fuel | cruel | level | *(spirit)* |
| | | | | | | | | |
| excel | expel | compel | impel | repel | cancel | travel | shrivel | |
| | | | | | | | | |
| channel | tunnel | flannel | quarrel | barrel | vessel | squirrel | tassel | |
| | | | | | | | | |
| caramel | enamel | parallel | spaniel | | | | | |

## WORDLIST (3) AL WORDS

| | | | | | | | | |
|---|---|---|---|---|---|---|---|---|
| local | floral | royal | fatal | total | postal | mental | rural | dental |
| final | loyal | moral | spiral | crystal | signal | mortal | pedal | rascal |
| equal | formal | legal | regal | canal | central | trial | dismal | real |
| | | | | | | | | |
| natural | personal | liberal | general | annual | manual | trivial | funeral | arrival |
| interval | capital | terminal | casual | actual | factual | punctual | usual | horizontal |
| animal | festival | capital | material | original | social | internal | external | removal |
| mineral | survival | rehearsal | criminal | national | recital | cathedral | hospital | admiral |
| | | | | | | | | |
| musical | political | typical | mechanical | medical | critical — *and all IC plus AL words.* | | | |

The next two lists cover the particular problem of words ending in ABLE and IBLE.

## WORDLIST (4) ABLE WORDS

| | | | | | | | | |
|---|---|---|---|---|---|---|---|---|
| able | stable | fable | usable | lovable | durable | suitable | reliable | disable |
| miserable | valuable | agreeable | advisable | curable | honourable | pliable | capable | dependable |
| viable | probable | perishable | constable | vegetable | creditable | noticeable | durable | reasonable |
| unbelievable | disagreeable | incurable | unrecognizable — *and many other opposites.* | | | | | |

## WORDLIST (5) IBLE WORDS (There are *far* fewer of these)

| | | | | | | | | |
|---|---|---|---|---|---|---|---|---|
| audible | credible | digestible | edible | sensible | responsible | legible | visible | forcible |
| horrible | defensible | terrible | possible | contemptible | invincible | incredible — *and other opposites.* | | |

## WORDLIST (6) OTHER SIMILAR WORDS

| | | | | | | | | | |
|---|---|---|---|---|---|---|---|---|---|
| ILE: | missile | hostile | agile | fertile | docile | exile | senile | juvenile | compile |
| | imbecile | defile | beguile | reconcile | crocodile | | | | |
| IL: | pencil | daffodil | utensil | fulfil | instil | distil | peril | *(Also notice* despoil*)* | |
| OL: | carol | extol | alcohol | | | | | | |

# EXERCISES

(a)  In each of the following sentences there are three words that have EL, AL or LE as their ending. Write out the sentence, putting the correct ending on the words. Underline the words you have completed.
   (1)  He always likes to trav.. by ped.. cyc.. .
   (2)  There is no need to be gent.. with a scoudr.. and a rasc.. .
   (3)  She could not help admiring the twink.. of that roy.. jew.. .
   (4)  I bought a litt.. sign.. for my mod.. railway.
   (5)  Architecturally, the steep.. of the cathedr.. is a marv.. .
   (6)  She started a quarr.. in the midd.. of the rehears.. .
   (7)  A rectang.. has two pairs of parall.. and equ.. sides.
   (8)  Nation.. fu.. consumption is expected to doub.. this year.
   (9)  The secret pan.. used by the crimin.. continued to baff.. detectives totally.
   (10)  The centr.. plot of this nov.. is naturally far from simp.. .                    (15)

(b)  In this exercise you have to choose between ABLE and IBLE endings.  Once again underline the words you select from the choice in the brackets.
   (1)  A (horrible, horrable) noise was (audible, audable) beneath.
   (2)  It is (probable, probible) that the site will prove (unsuitable, unsuitible).
   (3)  Though his disease is sadly (incurible, incurable), he continues to show (invincible, invinceable) optimism.
   (4)  This alternative is neither politically (credable, credible), nor economically (viable, vyible).
   (5)  Could some (invisible, invisable) force really have been (capible, capable) of kindling the fire?
   (6)  All (perishable, perishible) goods must be unloaded as soon as (possable, possible).
   (7)  The action of the (constible, constable) in separating the quarrelling men was very (creditible, creditable).
   (8)  She is personally (responsable, responsible) for negotiating a (durable, durible) settlement to this problem.
   (9)  You French may think the snail is (edible, edable); I think it is most (disagreeible, disagreeable).
   (10)  No (sensable, sensible) English person would ever actually swallow such an (indigestable, indigestible) morsel.                    (20)

(c)  In exercises (a) and (b) there are *ten* words which have been formed from AL, EL or LE words, by putting an *ending* on to them. Find the words, and make a list of them.                    (5)

(d)  In the following sentences *all* the AL, EL, LE, ABLE and IBLE words have been spelt wrong. Rewrite the sentences, putting them right. *Half* of the words are not included in the Wordlists opposite, so you will need to use your dictionary.
   (1)  The castel was brisseling with formidabel fortifications.
   (2)  The country yokle with his mongral dog comes to the carnivel.
   (3)  The barrals and bottels were hurriedly loaded on to the small vessal.
   (4)  The disposle of industrile waste in the canile is unacceptible.
   (5)  I shall need my specticles if I am to read that scribbal.
   (6)  The ornamentle trees in their respectabel gardens take on new autumle shades.
   (7)  We have encountered a cylindricel obstacal.                    (10)

# SPELLING TESTS

| 1 | 2 | 3 | 4 | 5 |
|---|---|---|---|---|
| idle | axle | people | double | cradle |
| parcel | jewel | material | punctual | novel |
| thistle | parallel | noticeable | rustle | measles |
| travel | national | prickle | rehearsal | arrival |
| typical | hurtle | vehicle | resemble | article |
| wriggle | agreeable | channel | reliable | mechanical |
| lovable | icicle | survival | tunnel | unbelievable |
| forcible | legible | defensible | impossible | irresponsible |
| fulfil | peril | audible | imbecile | unrecognizable |
| alcohol | incredible | crocodile | juvenile | daffodil |

   Do not be put off by the very long words. Break them down into sections, and they are not particularly difficul
When learning them, concentrate on the bits *you* usually get wrong (S instead of Z; IBLE instead of ABLE and so on)

# ABSTRACT NOUN ENDINGS

We are still on the subject of endings, but this time the endings of *abstract nouns*. These are words that stand for qualities, feelings, emotions, actions etc. — things which are not solid.

The most common ending for abstract nouns is probably NESS. With most words you just add NESS to the end of the word (normally an adjective):— *dark, darkness; sad, sadness.*

If the word already ends in N, you still add NESS (*mean — meanness* — double N); if the word ends in a SILENT E, you still add NESS (*like — likeness*).

BUT — if the word ends in a Y, change Y to I and then add NESS (*lazy, laziness; ugly, ugliness*).

The NESS ending presents few problems in spelling, but be careful about adding it to any adjective. Many have their own forms of abstract nouns — *hunger* not 'hungriness'; *sorrow* not 'sorriness' — or else form their abstract nouns with a different ending.

There are many abstract nouns that end in MENT, SHIP, DOM and TUDE. The same principles apply in adding these endings as for NESS:— *enjoy, enjoyment; judge, judgement;* — and other words where MENT is not so much an ending as part of the word, like *regiment* and *element*. Then there are *fellowship, friendship; kingdom, freedom, childhood, knighthood; multitude* and *gratitude*. Notice that TH is also an abstract noun ending:— *width, strength, health* etc.

When you are adding an ending that begins with a vowel, like AGE and URE, remember to remove silent E first if necessary. Otherwise, once again, the same principles apply:— *creature* (from *create*), *departure* (depart); *package, postage, marriage* (from *marry* with a Y).

Not all the words with these endings are abstract nouns of course, but they have been put together in the Wordlist to make learning them easier.

## WORDLIST

**NESS**
darkness
illness
weakness
greyness
leanness
greenness
likeness
soreness

**INESS**
laziness
ugliness
nastiness
happiness
emptiness
heaviness
business
dryness (!)

*Notice:—*
**ESS** *not* **NESS**
access (CC/SS)
success (CC/SS)
caress
excess
duress
recess

**SHIP**
fellowship
friendship
companionship
worship

**MENT**
improvement
statement
basement
pavement
atonement
contentment
attachment
involvement
agreement
payment
excitement
enjoyment
deployment
entertainment
treatment
encouragement
discouragement
advertisement
judgement
arrangement
establishment
postponement
detachment
replacement
punishment
nourishment
accomplishment
garment
fragment
moment
cement
testament
implement (E)
compartment
apartment
argument (! NO E)

**MENT** *plus some additions!*
monument
monumental
department
departmental
regiment
regimental
ornament
ornamental
supplement (E)
supplementary
element
elemental
elementary
compliment (I)
complimentary
parliament (! — IA)
parliamentary

**TUDE**
aptitude
magnitude
multitide
solitude
servitude
attitude
altitude
latitude
longitude
rectitude
fortitude
gratitude

*Notice also verbs in* **UDE**
conclude
exclude
include
intrude
protrude

**DOM**
kingdom
freedom
wisdom
random
seldom

**HOOD**
boyhood
girlhood
manhood
womanhood
childhood
adulthood
motherhood
brotherhood
parenthood
nationhood
priesthood
statehood
likelihood

**URE**
pleasure
creature
failure
departure
moisture
picture
capture
lecture
puncture
treasure (EA)
furniture
scripture
nature
pressure

**URE** *continued*
procure
procurement
pasture
pasturage
secure
security
insure
insurance
agriculture
agricultural

**AGE**
savage
damage
average
mortgage (! silent T)
heritage
sausage
patronage
garage
village
package
postage
foliage
assuage (!)
percentage
message
courage
hostage
baggage
advantage
image
cabbage
wreckage
mirage (!)

**EGE**
college
privilege
knowledge (EDGE)

## EXERCISES

(a) Make abstract nouns from the following words. (Make sure you put on the right ending — or make whatever other change is needed.)

| replace | moisten | hard | nation | friend |
|---------|---------|---------|--------|--------|
| please | like | punish | busy | angry | (10)

(b) In the following sentences complete the abstract nouns with the correct endings.
(1) The late depart.... of the train was due to a block... on the line.
(2) I require a replace.... for the missing pack... .
(3) I have great pleas... in presenting you with this award in grati.... for your years of service.
(4) The likeli.... of an improve.... in his condition is slight.
(5) We can only assume the fail... of the treat.... .
(6) Good.... is the only measure of wis... .
(7) Friend.... is a treas... beyond price.
(8) We have provided some entertain.... for your enjoy.... .
(9) The percent... of moist... in the atmosphere is carefully controlled.
(10) The silli.... of that child is only equalled by his lazi.... .  (10)

(c) In this exercise there are twenty words in *italics*. Ten of these are spelt right, and ten are spelt wrong, or have the wrong form or ending. Write out the sentences with the mistakes corrected, and then make a list of the correct words, a list of the wrongly spelt words, and finally a list of your corrections to them.
(1) The *leaness* of the meat is an *advantage* in cooking this dish.
(2) She showed *resentment* over the *longness* of her wait.
(3) I have sent a full *regimental detachment* to the ceremony.
(4) Some *agricultureal* strokes inflicted severe *punishment* on the bowling.
(5) With great *heaviness* of heart I looked up at the gates of the *collage* I was to attend for the next seven years.
(6) The force of the *elements* was a strong *discouragment* to our journey.
(7) What are the *arrangments* for the release of our *hostages*?
(8) I look forward to the *establishment* of the *brothership* of nations.
(9) My *marage* has brought me only *happiness*.
(10) Your *mesage* concerning the *success* of our bid was most welcome.  (20)

(d) Write out the following sentences, choosing the correct word from the choices offered you in the brackets.
(1) He was hidden in the thick (folliage, foliege, foliage).
(2) Slowly the hideous (creature, createure, creture) approached us.
(3) Have you put the car in the (garriage, garage, garredge), dear?
(4) We will have to arrange for the (postponment, postponement, posponement) of the professor's lecture.
(5) Who ordered two tons of liquid (sament, ciment, cement) to be poured on the drive?
(6) We are all under great (pressure, presure, preshure) at the moment.
(7) What (implement, impliment, empliment) was employed by the murderer?
(8) She has shown great (curage, courrage, courage) in the face of suffering.
(9) Sally has some (complementary, complimentary, complimentry) tickets for the ballet tomorrow night.
(10) (Elementary, elemental, alimentary), my dear Watson.  (10)

## SPELLING TESTS

| 1 | 2 | 3 | 4 | 5 |
|---|---|---|---|---|
| illness | greenness | emptiness | business | dryness |
| excess | success | access | friendship | worship |
| basement | employment | advertisement | accomplishment | cement |
| detachment | apartment | encouragement | payment | appointment |
| regimental | parliament | elementary | monument | gratitude |
| magnitude | attitude | freedom | wisdom | include |
| priesthood | likelihood | creature | moisture | treasure |
| pressure | furniture | secure | insure | percentage |
| village | courage | security | insurance | wreckage |
| college | privilege | message | advantage | knowledge |

Apart from NESS, there are very many abstract nouns that end in ION. Most of these are formed from verbs. There are three main forms of this ending:— ATION, TION and SION.

Many but not all of the ATION nouns come from verbs that end in ATE:— *separate — separation; locate — location; associate — association;* but also *invite — invitation.*

The TION ending is less common, and mainly comes in two forms:— CTION (*instruct — instruction; protect — protection*), and ITION (*compose — composition; add — addition*). There are others, though:— *intend — intention; digest — digestion.*

The SION ending is linked with verbs that already end in S — together with UDE, EDE, IDE, and IT:— *discuss — discussion; conclude — conclusion, decide — decision; submit — submission.* Notice that verbs ending in MIT always form nouns ending in MISSION — double S.

## WORDLIST

### ATE and ATION

dictate — dictation
create — creation
allocate — allocation
educate — education
moderate — moderation
situate — situation
operate — operation
relate — relation
nominate — nomination
tolerate — toleration
cremate — cremation

appreciation
ventilation
navigation
cultivation
imitation
association
compensation
co-operation (! hyphen)
celebration
calculation
congregation
acceleration (!CC = CS)
accommodation
commemoration
communication
evaporation
congratulation
contamination
penetration
translation
frustration
generation
regulation
aggravation
agitation
circulation
separation
initiation (TI = 'SH' sound)
illumination
participation
extermination
intoxication

*Notice also some other ION words:—*

companion
region

### ATION and OTHER VERBS

inform — information
observe — observation
reserve — reservation
imagine — imagination
tempt — temptation
combine — combination
explain — explanation (!)
invite — invitation
occupy — occupation
explore — exploration
determine — determination
consider — consideration
found — foundation
sense — sensation
apply — application (!)
despair — desperation (!)

### SOME OTHER ATE WORDS

climate
debate
private *and* privation
temperate
fortunate
passionate
affectionate
candidate
magistrate

### SOME OTHER ATION WORDS

nation
ration
salvation
station

### SIMILAR TION WORDS

motion
commotion (double M)
fraction
portion
proportion
section

champion
union

### TION

depose — deposition
compose — composition
oppose — opposition
add — addition
define — definition
object — objection
except — exception
direct — direction
connect — connection/connexion
reduce — reduction
receive — reception (!)
attend — attention
act — action
complete — completion
detain — detention
retain — retention
solve — solution
resolve — resolution
pollute — pollution

### SION

submit — submission
permit — permission
commit — commission

provide — provision
decide — decision
include — inclusion
concede — concession

express — expression
impress — impression
discuss — discussion
possess — possession
depress — depression

### OTHER SION WORDS

occasion    excursion
pension     passion
vision

suspicion
onion

### ADDITIONAL WORDS

graduation (UA)
location
dislocation
examination
immigration (MM)
emigration (one M)
implication
inoculation (not NN)
vaccination (double C)
conversation
subordination
exasperation
delegation
respiration
segregation

attraction
reaction
satisfaction

supposition
definition
exhibition (!H)
digestion
intention
invention

election
selection
protection
destruction
production
affection

dissolution
evolution
solution

procession
conclusion
conversion
persuasion (! UA)
division

million
fashion

opinion
religion

50

## EXERCISES

(a) Give the abstract nouns (all with one or other of the ION endings) that are formed from the following verbs. You will need your dictionary, as not all of them are in the Wordlist.

| | | | | |
|---|---|---|---|---|
| direct | determine | complete | educate | emit |
| eliminate | possess | inform | impose | edit |
| communicate | provide | connect | deduce | pretend |
| repress | tempt | define | destroy | act (10) |

(b) This exercise is the other way round. Give the verbs that these abstract nouns have been formed from. Once again, not all are in the Wordlist.

| | | | | |
|---|---|---|---|---|
| intention | delegation | destruction | dissolution | procession |
| evaporation | combination | sensation | attention | rationalization |
| exhibition | permission | division | invention | reception |
| constitution | deception | recitation | progression | delusion (10) |

(c) In the following sentences, choose the correct spelling from the alternatives you are given in the brackets. Underline the words you select.

(1) We hope for the (complesion, complition, completion) of the work next year.

(2) Have you arranged for the (connection, conection, connectation) of the electricity supply?

(3) The (nominition, nomination, nominasion) of the candidate will be tomorrow.

(4) Please accept our (congratulations, congratulasions, congratulitions) on your appointment to the post.

(5) Make sure you give your new boss a good (impretion, impresion, impression).

(6) Today, I would like you to write a (composision, composation, composition).

(7) Do you boys have (permition, permission, permision) to go home early?

(8) I am suffering from (depresion, depretion, depression) at the moment.

(9) There is a great deal of (opposition, opposision, opposission) to the proposal before us.

(10) Who is responsible for the (commotation, commition, commotion) in this class? (10)

(d) In the following extract from a story twenty of the abstract nouns have been changed so that they are now incorrect in form or spelling. Rewrite the passage, putting things right. Underline the words you have changed.

> Theresa waited eagerly for her ordishon. This was the height of her ambission so far, the result of her long educatoin in the ballet. She had made the resolvation to be a dancer when she was six, and since then her life had been one of applicasion and determinition. At first there had been many deprevations, and few compensashuns. Though she had suffered moments of depresion, her intension had never really wavered, however much others had exercised their powers of persuation. Now she finally had the satisfacsion of success. She had received the invition to be seen by Madame Romanova. Only a fraxion of the total number of people got this far; and of those only a small proporsion could be accepted. In the end her selexion or exclution would be decided today. She shivered in apprehention. This was far worse than any examinasion. Suddenly she heard a clapping of hands.
>
> "Come forward, girl. Take up your posision!" — It was now or never. (20)

## SPELLING TESTS

| 1 | 2 | 3 | 4 | 5 |
|---|---|---|---|---|
| education | ration | fraction | station | motion |
| addition | nation | agitation | initiation | pollution |
| division | objection | correction | decision | definition |
| creation | situation | occupation | communication | application |
| exception | vision | affectionate | impression | supposition |
| co-operation | affectionate | passionate | appreciation | participation |
| commission | magistrate | dissolution | destruction | inclusion |
| concede | supposition | persuade | navigation | desperation |
| concession | onion | persuasion | completion | possession |
| fashion | union | religion | region | section |

51

# FACTSHEET TWENTY-SIX    ABSTRACT NOUNS — ITY, TY, CY AND Y

The third particularly important batch of ABSTRACT NOUNS are those ending in ITY. Many are formed by adding this ending to adjectives, such as those in AL (*local — locality; moral — morality*). When adding ITY to words with SILENT E, remember to remove the E (*secure — security, pure — purity*).

There are a few variations to ITY, such as plain TY (*bounty, liberty, beauty*). Many of these, and some ITY words, exist in their own right; they are not another word plus an ending. Also be careful with the smaller number of words ending in ETY (*safety, anxiety*), CY (*policy, accuracy*) and SY (*courtesy*).

Adjectives ending in ABLE (see Factsheet Twenty-three) often form nouns ending in ABILITY (*capable — capability*), while IBLE words have, of course, IBILITY (*responsible — responsibility*).

There are very many other English words ending in Y, most of which are easy to spell. In particular there are adjectives like *dainty, curly, muddy, dirty* (which, as you already know, often have their own abstract nouns ending in NESS — *daintiness, dirtiness* etc.). If you are putting a Y ending on a word remember to remove any silent E's (*wave — wavy*).

Another group of Y words are verbs ending in IFY (like *modify* and *rectify*).

## WORDLIST

### ITY WORDS

locality
morality
hospitality
totality
fatality
nationality
conformity
stupidity
electricity
minority
majority
authority
similarity
humanity
familiarity
solemnity
priority
seniority
security
obscurity
diversity
severity
fertility
sincerity
hostility
maturity
opportunity
university
purity
infinity
activity
agility
calamity
captivity
capacity
fidelity
quality
quantity
gravity
charity
dignity
nativity
unity
city

### SOME ITY WORDS TO WATCH

| | |
|---|---|
| prosperity | (prosperous) |
| simplicity | (simple) |
| emnity (!) | (enemy) |
| eternity | (eternal) |
| equity | (equal) |
| jollity | (jolly) |
| brevity | (brief) |
| nobility | (noble) |
| ferocity | (ferocious) |
| curiosity | (curious) |
| necessity | (necessary) |

### TY WORDS

| | |
|---|---|
| duty | poverty |
| bounty | honesty |
| beauty (!) | novelty |
| county | modesty |
| liberty | sovereignty |
| majesty | certainty |
| casualty (UA) | treaty |
| loyalty | royalty |

### ETY WORDS

| | |
|---|---|
| safety | |
| nicety | |
| surety | |
| society | |
| piety | (pious) |
| anxiety | (anxious) |
| variety | (various) |
| notoriety | (notorious) |
| gaiety | (gay) |

### CY WORDS

| | |
|---|---|
| piracy | privacy |
| confederacy | accuracy |
| legacy | lunacy |
| policy | secrecy |
| conspiracy | fallacy |

### SY WORDS

courtesy
hypocrisy
ecstasy (no X)

### ABILITY WORDS

ability
stability
durability
reliability
liability
capability
suitability
probability
profitability
disability
advisability

### IBILITY WORDS

possibility
reponsibility
visibility
credibility
legibility
fallibility
sensibility
  (*check the meaning before you use this!*)

### SOME OTHER Y NOUNS

| | |
|---|---|
| tragedy | destiny |
| comedy | tyranny |
| melody | colony |
| malady | company |
| subsidy | mutiny |
| remedy | agony |
| academy | villainy |
| enemy | ceremony |
| astronomy | botany |
| anatomy | symphony |
| energy | galaxy |
| family | trophy |
| sympathy | canopy |

forty (!)
eighty (!)
ninety (!)
*etc.*

### DOUBLE CONSONANT PLUS Y

| | |
|---|---|
| carry | berry |
| tarry | cherry |
| marry | ferry |
| hurry | lorry |
| scurry | jolly |
| furry | jelly |
| worry | merry |
| sorry | pretty |
| happy | petty |
| starry | jetty |
| silly | sunny |
| penny | funny |

*Notice:—*

| | |
|---|---|
| money | pulley |
| honey | jockey |

alley (narrow passage)
ally   (friendly nation)

### SINGLE CONSONANT PLUS Y

| | |
|---|---|
| ivy | crazy |
| lady | wary |
| baby | vary |
| rosy | shiny |
| cosy | tiny |
| gravy | any |
| navy | many |
| study | copy |
| bury | fury |
| defy | deny |
| ordinary | hasty |
| contrary | nasty |
| guilty | mouldy |

### SOME FY VERBS

| | |
|---|---|
| terrify | amplify |
| horrify | rectify |
| testify | dignify |
| modify | clarify |
| identify | glorify |

*Note:— Some have abstract nouns ending in IFICATION:—*

identification
modification
amplification

## EXERCISES

a) Rewrite the following sentences using an abstract noun instead of an adjective. Here is an example:— "What nation does she come from?" becomes "What is her nationality?"

    (1)   Is your journey necessary?

         Is there any ........... for your journey?

    (2)   She is the country's sovereign.

         She has ........... over the country.

    (3)   I am destined to great things.

         My ........... is to great things.

    (4)   Mandy prefers various colours.

         Mandy prefers a ........... of colours.

    (5)   They conspired to commit the crime.

         There was a ........... to commit the crime.

    (6)   He is a very pious man.

         He is a man of great ........... .

    (7)   You are the most senior person.

         You have the greatest ........... .

    (8)   I believe that it is possible.

         I believe in its ........... .

    (9)   He is not a reliable witness.

         As a witness he lacks ........... .

    (10)  She is being held captive.

         She is being held in ........... .       (10)

b) Write out the following sentences, selecting the correct choice from those in the brackets. Underline the words you choose.

    (1)   His accident was a terrible (tragedy, tradegy).

    (2)   He is now suffering from a severe (disility, disability).

    (3)   I was amused by the (novlety, novelty) of her act.

    (4)   My (loyalty, loyality) to the crown is beyond question.

    (5)   You should always wear clothing with high (visability, visibility).

    (6)   He used to be Secretary for the (Colonies, Colinies).

    (7)   I have my doubts about his (suitibility, suitability) for the post.

    (8)   I cannot, however, deliver an opinion with any (certainty, certainity).

    (9)   Do you accept full (responsability, responsibility) for the decision?

    (10)  Your writing is a masterpiece of (illegibility, illegability).       (10)

c) Rewrite each of the sentences in Exercise (b) using the appropriate adjective in place of the abstract nouns. This is the reverse of what you did in Exercise (a). For example: "I accept the necessity of these measures" would become "I accept that these measures are necessary." You may have to make quite considerable changes, but you must use an adjective linked to the abstract noun, and you must keep the meaning the same.    (10)

d) In the following excerpt from a story there are twenty words that have been mis-spelt. Write out the passage correcting these mistakes.

    The ivvy covered the acadamy's walls and hung around the windows of the studdies. The famly were obviously impressed by the antiquety of the buildings. I couldn't denny that I was quite impressed too, but I wouldn't abandon my hostilty to my forthcoming captivety within those sturdie walls.

    "It has a distinct similarty to a prison," I muttered. "Those walls look moldy to me, and the whole place smells of dried up gravvy and old cabbage."

    "I won't have that sort of stupidety, my lad," replied my father briskly. "Anyone would think you were terified of the idea. In all probility you'll enjoy every moment of it."

    His jolity lacked credability even to my mother, who glanced around with renewed anxity. I seized my opportunety.

    "Why can't I go to an ordinery school?" I demanded.       (20)

## SPELLING TESTS

| 1 | 2 | 3 | 4 | 5 |
|---|---|---|---|---|
| bounty | duty | any | defy | curious |
| guilty | beauty | navy | identify | curiosity |
| money | bury | ferocious | identification | fury |
| enemy | berry | ferocity | necessary | furry |
| emnity | energy | tragedy | necessity | glorify |
| sincerity | tyranny | privacy | anxiety | society |
| honesty | various | casualty | courtesy | authority |
| agility | variety | suitability | simplicity | secrecy |
| seniority | capacity | familiarity | capability | probability |
| nationality | opportunity | legibility | visibility | responsibility |

The next problem endings we have to look at are AR and ER; OR and OUR; and RE. By far the most common is ER. It occurs in verbs (*enter, conquer*), adjectives (*clever, eager*), nouns (*ladder, weather*), and other parts of speech (*ever, after*).

In particular notice that it is used to form the comparatives of adjectives (the form that means 'more something' — *better, brighter, heavier, holier*). The superlative, or 'most' form of adjectives of course ends in EST — *best, brightest, heaviest* etc.

Many ER words stand for 'agents' or jobs; and 'instruments' or tools: *worker, teacher; hammer, poker*.

That is the main problem, because many of these also end in OR:— *visitor, doctor; radiator*.

The other endings are fairly small groups, with words like *centre* (RE), *colour* (OUR), *calendar* (AR), *engineer* (EER — a variation on ER!).

There is also a group of nouns ending in ARY, ERY, ORY, URY — and just plain RY. Examples of these are also included in the Wordlist.

## WORDLIST

**ER**
enter, plaster, render, leather, linger, weather, conquer, tiger, wither, silver, gather, winter, deliver, larder, alter, supper, discover, letter, flutter, ladder, mutter, rubber, stutter, poker, utter, ruler, suffer, cruiser, bitter, computer, upper, laughter, clever, matter, other, quarter, either, remainder, neither, surrender, ever, grandmother, after, grandfather, over, drawer, altogether, chapter, however, thunder, rather, another, whether, water, powder, slaughter, cover, newspaper, shoulder, sober, corner, Easter, shelter, September, power, October, shower, November, register, December

**PEOPLE AND JOBS (AGENTS):**

*ER WORDS:* member, master, passenger, minister, customer, ruler, robber, murderer, prisoner, driver, employer, officer, writer, messenger, worker, partner, stranger, soldier, brewer, grocer, teacher, farmer, miner, builder, lawyer (!), gardener, plumber, plasterer, undertaker, waiter, commuter, explorer, adviser

*OR WORDS:* doctor, tailor, sailor, author, tutor, debtor, creditor, conductor, instructor, emperor, governor, solicitor, visitor, senator, warrior (!), mayor (!), operator, proprietor, inventor, visitor, bachelor, victor, traitor, investor, impostor, creator, councillor, counsellor, ancestor, vendor, actor

**OTHER OR WORDS:** motor, razor, radiator, escalator, indicator, elevator, transistor, anchor, mirror, corridor, reactor, error, terror, junior, senior, interior, exterior, superior, inferior

**EER WORDS:** auctioneer, buccaneer, musketeer, engineer, pioneer, mountaineer, veneer, career

**ORE WORDS:** carnivore, herbivore

**AR WORDS:** altar, calendar, grammar, beggar, scholar, cigar, vinegar, pillar, liar, burglar (!), cellar, regular, popular, singular, peculiar, familiar, circular, similar

**OUR WORDS:** colour, armour, favour, flavour, honour, harbour, labour, rumour, humour, vapour, neighbour, behaviour, endeavour

**ARY WORDS:** library, military, missionary, boundary, burglary, salary, January, February, ordinary, necessary, primary, auxiliary

**ERY WORDS:** bravery, grocery, nursery, machinery, jewellery, mystery

**ORY WORDS:** factory, memory, history, victory, story, glory

**URY WORDS:** century, injury, perjury, treasury, jury, fury

**RY WORDS:** cavalry, infantry, rivalry, industry, chemistry, registry, laundry, poultry, country, poetry, tapestry

*There are a few RE WORDS:—* acre centre theatre sabre worse (worst!) manoeuvre
*And do not forget the comparatives:—* better upper higher easier friendlier

54

## EXERCISES

(a) Choose the correct spellings from the words in the brackets. Underline these words when you write out the sentences.

(1) Send a (messenger, messengor) for the (docter, doctor), (master, mastor); the (engineor, engineer) has been struck by a fly-wheel.

(2) The prosecution (lawyer, loyer) claimed that the defendant was not only a (rober, robber) and (burgler, burglar), but also a (murder, murderer).

(3) The (inventor, inventer) failed to persuade the (visitors, visiters) to become (investors, investers) in his new (computor, computer).

(4) I shall need a (plummer, plumber) and then a (plasterer, plaster) to complete the installation of the (radiatres, radiators) in the (librery, library).

(5) The (factary, factory) (inspectres, inspectors) have decided to report the (proprietors, proprieters) to the (ministory, ministry).

(6) The (color, colour) on the (indicator, indicater) was red, and the whole (seller, cellar) was already filled with choking (vaper, vapour).

(7) We shall be sending a (circulor, circular) to all our (regular, reguler) (customers, customars) to see how (populer, popular) this product is likely to be.

(8) The (officeor, officer) gave (ordres, orders) to his (soljers, soldiers) to arrest the (traiter, traitor).

(9) The (interiar, interior) (decoraters, decorators) have for some reason decided to mount the bathroom (mirrow, mirror) in the (corridor, corrider).

(10) There is a (rumour, rumer) that if our (behavier, behaviour) is good, the class will be taken to the (theater, theatre) just before we break up for the (Eastre, Easter) holidays. (20)

(b) Here is a selection of words, to which can be added either ER or OR. Your task is to select the right ending for each of them. Be careful: you may have to make *other* changes in the spelling as well as attaching the ending.

| | | | | |
|---|---|---|---|---|
| rule | destroy | begin | elect | settle |
| brew | remind | remain | sin | conduct |
| distribute | sculpt | explore | distil | carry |
| transform | indicate | create | war | empire (10) |

(c) Here is some more of the story (about an American boy at an English boarding school) that you had in the last Worksheet. Once again, your job is to correct the twenty spelling mistakes you will find in it.

My school carere began in the librery with an interview with the headmastor. This superier being soon made the discovry that I did not know much by British standards, and though I was a teenajor I was allocated to the most juniar form. Next I was taken to the dormitary by my partnor — which meant the pupil in the uper bunk, directly above me. He would be my instructer in the machinary of the school routine and regulations. I rapidly learnt from my fellow border that things were even werse than I had imagined. It was not just prison I was going to sufer; the sentence included hard labor too. By the time the other 'scholers' — complete with their extraordinery uniforms — arrived, I was shaking in terrer, and praying for the arrival of the U.S. cavalry. Of course my youthful councillor had exaggerated — but not much.

You may have found twenty-one mistakes, — but one of them is a genuine *American* spelling. Bonus marks if your can say which one it is! (20)

## SPELLING TESTS

| 1 | 2 | 3 | 4 | 5 |
|---|---|---|---|---|
| other | weather | either | liar | ruler |
| water | whether | newspaper | leather | centre |
| slaughter | passenger | burglar | December | register |
| soldier | interior | corridor | builder | peculiar |
| warrior | grocer | employer | debtor | reactor |
| proprietor | ancestor | vinegar | neighbour | messenger |
| gardener | commuter | heavier | circular | pioneer |
| creator | bachelor | lawyer | engineer | behaviour |
| treasury | endeavour | solicitor | grocery | chemistry |
| library | missionary | machinery | auxiliary | mystery |

We are still on endings, and this time we begin with words that end in ENT and ENCE — or ANT and ANCE. The NT words are usually adjectives; the NCE words usually nouns.

The ones with E are most common (such as *intelligent, obedient, consequence, confidence*); so treat ENT/ENCE as the rule, and learn the exceptions that have ANT/ANCE (words like *distant, important, defiance, extravagance*).

Notice also that there are some nouns that end in ENCY and ANCY (*tendency* and *tenancy*), and some additional adjectives that end in ENTIAL and ANTIAL (*influential, substantial*).

## WORDLIST

### ENT WORDS

| | |
|---|---|
| silent | silence |
| absent | absence |
| insolent | insolence |
| evident | evidence |
| innocent | innocence |
| consequent | consequence |
| intelligent | intelligence |
| magnificent | magnificence |
| violent | violence |
| convenient | convenience |
| obedient | obedience |
| urgent | urgency |
| frequent | frequency |
| transparent | transparency |
| sufficient | sufficiency |
| efficient | efficiency |
| decent | decency |
| consistent | consistency |

### ANT WORDS

| | |
|---|---|
| distant | distance |
| important | importance |
| abundant | abundance |
| defiant | defiance |
| ignorant | ignorance |
| arrogant | arrogance |
| elegant | elegance |
| fragrant | fragrance |
| extravagant | extravagance |
| assistant | assistance |
| constant | constancy |
| infant | infancy |
| tenant | tenancy |
| vacant | vacancy |

*Do not forget*:—

dependant (*noun*) dependent (*adj.*)
independent (*ENT*) *and* independence

### ENTIAL and ANTIAL

confident — confidence — confidential
existent — existence — existential
different — difference — differential

influence — influential

substance — substantial
circumstance — circumstantial

### OTHER WORDS TO REMEMBER

parent — parental
accident — accidental
incident — incidental

defence   offence   pretence

appearance   insurance   balance
acquaintance   appliance   romance

## ISE, ICE AND IZE ENDINGS

Another group of endings that can be confused are ISE, IZE and ICE.

IZE on the whole is a verb ending (as in *organize* and *modernize*), and it therefore stays in nouns formed from such verbs (*organization, modernization*). But all the IZE and IZATION words *can* also be spelt ISE and ISATION. (*Organize* is sometimes spelt *organise*; *realise* and *realize* are both quite common.)

A few verbs can ONLY be spelt ISE (like *advise* and *exercise*). See the Wordlist!

ICE is normally a noun ending (as in *office* and *justice*), but you find it on some words that can be noun or verb (like *notice*). Sometimes you find a noun spelt ICE, and its verb spelt ISE — like *practice* and *practise; advice* and *advise*.

## WORDLIST

### ISE WORDS

| | |
|---|---|
| advertise | chastise |
| comprise | revise |
| despise | devise |
| advise | disguise |
| exercise | surprise |
| surmise | |
| compromise | concise (adj.) |
| enterprise | precise (adj.) |
| | paradise (n.) |

### IZE WORDS

modernize
recognize
authorize
criticize
agonize
pulverize
civilize
sympathize

### ICE WORDS

notice
office
justice
service
sacrifice
prejudice
police

entice (v.)

### ICE (noun) and ISE (verb)

| | |
|---|---|
| device | devise |
| advice | advise |
| practice | practise |

### ISE *or* IZE!

realise *or* realize
organise *or* organize
*Remember that all IZE words can be spelt ISE*

## FUL ENDINGS

We have space for a note on one other ending that gives a vast amount of trouble for no reason at all. It is the ending FUL, used to form adjectives from nouns:— *thoughtful, helpful, plentiful*. All you have to remember is FUL not FULL; ONE L NOT TWO.

If you are adding it to words ending in Y, remember to change Y to I first!

## WORDLIST

| | | | | | |
|---|---|---|---|---|---|
| careful | dreadful | faithful | grateful | thoughtful | sorrowful |
| wonderful | plentiful | beautiful | dutiful | fanciful | merciful |

awful (! *no* E).   *Also notice* fulfil (!)

## EXERCISES

(a) In the following sentences, choose the correct spelling from the choices in brackets. Remember to underline the words you insert when you write out your answers.

(1) (Parents, parants), when thinking of their children, are well aware that (absance, absence) makes the heart grow fonder, but in the meantime (silense, silence) is undoubtedly golden.

(2) (Extravagance, extravagency) is an (inconveniant, inconvenient) vice when you also suffer from shortage of (sufficient, sufficant) funds.

(3) (Ignorence, ignorance) of the law is not regarded as a (sufficant, sufficient) (defense, defence), whereas these days the (flagrent, flagrant) (defiance, defience) of the law is (apparently, apparantly) claimed to be perfect justification.

(4) I am (confidant, confident) that we shall get the (vacent, vacant) (tenency, tenancy).

(5) The (circumstancial, circumstantial) (evidence, evidance) was very (influensial, influential) in convincing the jury that he was far from (innosent, innocent).                                                                         (20)

(b) In the following passage, your task is exactly the same. Choose the correct spellings from the choices given.

You must (sacrifise, sacrifice) your (prejudices, prejudises) and (recognize, recognise) that these outdated (practices, practises) must be changed. My (advice, advise) is to (device, devise) a (concice, concise) scheme to (modernise, modernize) your procedures. Of course you will have to (authorise, authorize) the complete (reorganization, reorganisation) of the (office, offise). A (thoughtful, thoughtfull) (advertizing, advertising) campaign should (fulfil, fullfil) your needs, so long as you avoid (fansiful, fanciful) and (extravagent, extravagant) claims. You could of course call in (independant, independent) (efficiancy, efficiency) (consultents, consultants) if you feel that my suggestions lack (balance, balence).

*Note: In four cases BOTH of the spellings could be correct! Make a list of these words.*                (20)

(c) The following words can be made into new nouns or adjectives by adding the ENT or ANT ending. Your job is to select the right ending for each word. You need to be very careful, though, as some of the words change their form a great deal in the process!

| | | | | |
|---|---|---|---|---|
| serve | pertain | remain | prevail | protest |
| equal | excel | ignore | differ | dominate    (5) |

(d) (i) Form a verb ending in IZE or ISE from each of the following:—

| | | | | |
|---|---|---|---|---|
| immortal | summary | factor | solemn | category |

(ii) Form a word ending in FUL, or FULL of course, from the following:—

| | | | | |
|---|---|---|---|---|
| joy | hope | bounty | plenty | cup    (5) |

## SPELLING TESTS

| 1 | 2 | 3 | 4 | 5 |
|---|---|---|---|---|
| assistant | silent | pretence | fragrant | awful |
| obedient | disguise | beautiful | fragrance | vacant |
| obedience | arrogant | tenant | intelligent | vacancy |
| defiant | arrogance | tenancy | intelligence | advice |
| defiance | efficient | influence | dutiful | advise |
| advertise | efficiency | influential | extravagant | advertise |
| sympathize | surprise | civilize | extravagance | violent |
| practice | prejudice | paradise | incidental | violence |
| practise | precise | authorize | accidental | despise |
| service | modernization | acquaintance | civilization | appearance |

You will be pleased to hear that this is the last one about endings! We will go through a few other endings that sometimes cause problems.

**LY** is used for forming adverbs. There is no reason it should be a problem, so long as you remember to change Y at the ends to I (*happy — happily*). If the word already ends in L, the adverb will have double L (*thoughtful — thoughtfully*).

The only thing to watch is words ending in LE (such as *single* and *double*) — they knock off the E and add Y (*doubly, singly*). There are a few others to beware of (*due — duly; dull — dully*) as you will see in the Wordlist.

**EN** and **ON**. Most adjectives (*golden, wooden*), verbs (*soften, chasten*), and the past participles (*taken, spoken*) end in EN, rather than ON.

A few nouns (*dozen, heaven, garden*) end in EN, but more end in ON (*bacon, weapon, matron, pardon, reason*).

**OUS** is quite a common adjective ending, as in *jealous, dangerous* etc. The alternative IOUS turns up:

(a)    in adjectives formed from TION words (*caution — cautious*)

(b)    following a C that sounds like S (*gracious, malicious*)

(c)    where you can clearly hear an EE-US sound (*previous*) — especially in words formed from Y words (*fury — furious*).

Notice that CIOUS always sounds like SHUS (just as TION sounds like SHUN). There are also a few tricky words with EOUS (like *courageous*, where the E is part of the GE!).

Some examples of many other word endings, that should not present any great problems, are also included in this particular Wordlist.

## WORDLIST

| LY | EN | ON | OUS | | IOUS | |
|---|---|---|---|---|---|---|
| seriously | shorten (!T) | lesson | prosperous | (prosperity) | anxious | (anxiety) |
| hopefully | moisten | sermon | generous | (generosity) | various | (variety) |
| slowly | soften | person | enormous | (enormity & | curious | (curiosity) |
| angrily | hasten | skeleton | | enormousness) | | |
| prettily | listen | bacon | marvellous | (!) (marvel) | victorious | (victory) |
| nicely | | matron | dangerous | (danger) | glorious | (glory) |
| wisely | kitten | prison | famous | (fame) | furious | (fury) |
| idly | woollen (!LL) | lemon (one M) | ridiculous | (ridicule) | | |
| steeply | heaven (EA) | iron (!) | nervous | (nerve) | cautious | (caution) |
| nobly | linen (one N) | reason | glamorous | (glamour) | suspicious | (suspicion) |
| | citizen | season | | | religious | (religion) |
| duly | siren | squadron | jealous | (jealousy) | gracious | (grace) |
| truly | burden | apron | | | malicious | (malice) |
| | oven | poison | numerous | | | |
| dully | hyphen (!Y) | weapon (EA) | preposterous | | previous | serious |
| fully | oxygen | | tremendous | | precious | delicious |

*Notice* EOUS: courageous, outrageous, courteous.

### SOME OTHER COMMON WORD ENDINGS TO KEEP IN MIND

| ACE | (rather than *ase*) | palace | embrace | surface | replace | necklace | (*but notice* purchase) |
|---|---|---|---|---|---|---|---|
| AIL | (rather than *ale*) | retail | detail | prevail | blackmail | (*but* female *and* nightingale) | |

| AY | betray | delay | display | repay | railway | subway | runway | stowaway |
|---|---|---|---|---|---|---|---|---|
| EY | convey | survey | obey | disobey | purvey (EY *is much less common!*) | | | |

| ETE | complete | concrete | obsolete | (*Notice:*— discrete (*separate*) and discreet (*tactful*).) | | |
|---|---|---|---|---|---|---|
| EAT | defeat | retreat | entreat | (*Notice* conceit *and* deceit) | | |

| EDE | concede | precede | impede | recede | intercede | supersede | stampede |
|---|---|---|---|---|---|---|---|
| EED | exceed | proceed | succeed | indeed | decreed (*past tense*) | | |

| UE | value | statue | avenue | issue | argue | rescue | pursue |
|---|---|---|---|---|---|---|---|
| EW | curfew | mildew | renew | nephew (!) | review (!) | | |

| INE | machine | quarantine | submarine | vaseline | routine | margarine (!) | nicotine |
|---|---|---|---|---|---|---|---|
| | medicine | famine | genuine | sanguine | | | |
| | combine | define | decline | divine | undermine | porcupine | crystalline (!) |
| ENE | serene *and* | obscene | EEN | foreseen *and* canteen | | EAN | demean *and* unclean |
| IN | margin | raisin | javelin | ruin | origin | violin | satin (!) |

## EXERCISES

(a) Rewrite the following sentences, employing an adjective ending in OUS, rather than the noun shown in italics. E.g. "We rejoiced in our *victory*" would become "We rejoiced that we had been *victorious*". Once again, underline the key word in your new sentence.

    (1)    His recovery is an absolute *marvel*.

    (2)    Before my interview I had terrible *nerves*.

    (3)    She showed irrational *jealousy* about John and Alice.

    (4)    My reaction to his offer was one of *suspicion* and *caution*.

    (5)    I was amazed at the *enormity* of his offence.

    (6)    She combines a lack of *grace* with a show of *malice*.

    (7)    He was full of *fury* that he had been held up to *ridicule*.    (10)

(b) Choose the correct spellings from the words in brackets. When you write out the sentences underline the words you have chosen.

    (1)    Put the (backen, bacon, bakon) in the (oven, ovon, ovin) to keep warm.

    (2)    We had to sit there and (lissen, listen, lisson) to a long (sermen, serman, sermon).

    (3)    Their (weppons, weppens, weapons) were made of (iorn, iern, iron).

    (4)    She held the (kitton, kiten, kitten) in her (apron, apren, appren).

    (5)    I am (fully, fuly, fuelly) persuaded that he has spoken (truely, trewly, truly).    (10)

(c) In the sentences of the following exercise there are twenty words mis-spelt. Write out the sentences correcting the mistakes.

    (1)    Our armies suffered compleat defete in the battle.

    (2)    I entreet you to be discrete in this matter in view of the possibility of deceipt by those involved.

    (3)    You will indede be exceding your authority if you impeed this inquiry in any way.

    (4)    My nefeu is currently revewing the valew of the statews in the family collection.

    (5)    They are to survay the route of the new railweigh.

    (6)    Gary is going to purchace a necklase for Samantha.

    (7)    Why was there no margarene available in the cantene today?

    (8)    That violine is a genuin antique.    (20)

(d) This is another exercise in choosing the correct spelling. This time none of the words are in the Wordlist, so you will need to use your dictionary. The first fifteen words are the same type as in the Wordlist, though — but the last five are not (just to test you . . .).

| | | |
|---|---|---|
| tamboureen/tambourine | gainsay/gainsey | betwene/between |
| wholesail/wholesale | arrey/array | courtale/curtail |
| replete/replite | urchin/urchine | mildue/mildew |
| convene/convean | unclean/unclene | ambigous/ambiguous |
| interveen/intervene | revenew/revenue | odeous/odious |
| repare/repair   beware/bewair   delite/delight | | excite/exsight   deseave/deceive   (10) |

## SPELLING TESTS

| 1 | 2 | 3 | 4 | 5 |
|---|---|---|---|---|
| lesson | canteen | margin | suspicion | anxious |
| moisten | skeleton | furious | machine | anxiety |
| delay | soften | lemon | nicely | defeat |
| survey | issue | kitten | iron | complete |
| seriously | hopefully | angrily | linen | nobly |
| victorious | caution | prosperous | review | squadron |
| nephew | cautious | prosperity | courageous | citizen |
| marvellous | dangerously | jealous | numerous | preposterous |
| margarine | courteous | dully | palace | generous |
| hyphen | oxygen | duly | purchase | generosity |

59

An ending on a word is called a *suffix*. Since we have seen quite enough of them, we shall now look at some *prefixes* — additions to the beginnings of words.

The most common prefixes are those that indicate a negative. They change the meaning of a word to its opposite. The chief of them is UN; in front of verbs (*unpack, unlock, undo*); and in front of many adjectives (*unable, unfortunate, unjust, unfriendly*); and adverbs (*unwisely*).

Another sort of negative (which often means 'badly' or 'wrongly') is MIS, as in *mistake, misfortune, misuse, misshapen* and *mis-spell*.

MIS and UN derive from old English; there are equivalents which derive from Latin — DIS and IN. IN is very common:— *incompetent, indirect, inevitable, injustice, insolent, invalid*. But you must learn these rules about it:—

In front of M, P or B — IN becomes IM:— *immoral, immortal, impossible, impatient, imbalance*.

In front of L — IN becomes IL (so you get double L):— *illegal, illiterate*.

In front of R — IN becomes IR:— *irrational, irregular, irrelevant*.

Sometimes the IN prefix means simply 'in', rather than 'not' (*inform, involve, inquest, infuriate*): the same rules apply, so you get *immediate, impact, illusion, irritate*.

Similar to IN meaning 'in' is EN meaning 'in': *entangle, engage, endure, entire, endanger*. The same rules apply to P and B (*embark, employ*) but NOT to R and L (*enrich, enlist*)!

There are also one or two words where NON is used to make opposites (*nonsense, non-fiction, non-stop*). Do not use it when there are other perfectly good opposites available.

Before we look at the Wordlist, if you are wondering what happened to DIS . . . wait till the next Factsheet!

## WORDLIST

| UN | MIS | IN | IMM | OTHER 'IN' WORDS |
|---|---|---|---|---|
| | | | | (*not negatives*) |
| unhealthy | misconstrue | inaccurate | immoral | |
| unforgivable | mistreat | inactive | immortal | intend |
| unsuccessful | mislead | inaudible | immune | inhabit |
| untrue | misprint | inconvenient | immunize | insult |
| unkind | mistrust | inconsistent | immature | instruct |
| unhappy | misplace | incomplete | immediate | inflammable |
| unbelievable | misuse | inevitable | | indicate |
| untidy | mishap | inconsiderate | IMP | infuriate |
| unsteady | mistake | incorrect | | involve |
| undone | mistook | incredible | impossible | institution |
| unsung | mistaken | inappropriate | improbable | intrigue (! GUE) |
| unwilling | | independent | impartial | information |
| unexpected | *Also notice:* | indirect | impassable | investigate |
| unemployed | mischief | inequality | imperfect | intensify |
| unwanted | mischievous | indifferent | impertinent | |
| unknown | | infirm | improper | immense |
| unseen | EN | infinite | impure | immerse |
| unlock | | inhuman | impatient | immediate |
| undo | enable | insensitive | imprecise | |
| unroll | enlarge | infrequent | | impact |
| untie | enclose | invisible | ILL | implore |
| unwind | encourage | invariable | | important |
| unload | engulf | insoluble | illegal | impose |
| unfasten | enlist | invalid | illiterate | impress |
| uncertain | enrol (one L) | insufficient | illegible | improve |
| unfortunate | enrich | insecure | | |
| unconscious | enthusiasm | insane | IRR | illusion |
| uncomfortable | envelop (*verb*) | indivisible | irrational | illustrate |
| | envelope (*noun*) | insensible | irregular | illustrious |
| | entangle | | irrelevant | |
| | | | irresponsible | irrigate |
| | | | | irritate |

*Notice some parallel opposites*:—
unable, disable, inability, disability          unjust: injustice          indirect: misdirect

inequality: unequal          undecided: indecisive          unfortunate: misfortune
unbelievable: disbelief          illusion *has its own opposite* disillusion.

*There are also*:— ensure (*make sure*): insure (*take out a policy*).

## EXERCISES

(a) For each of the following words form an opposite or contrary by adding the prefix UN or IN or MIS. Not all of the words are on the Factsheet, so check your answers in the dictionary.

| take | correct | represent | sensitive | real |
| cover | rest | sure | certain | decent |
| fortune | fortunate | sufficient | finished | complete |
| seen | visible | apprehension | | |
| to appropriate (verb) | appropriate (adjective) | | | (10) |

(b) Choose the correct spellings from the alternatives given you.

(1) Do not be (missled, misled, mislead), I (inplore, implore) you, by these false (ilusions, illusions).

(2) The way lies through an (immense, imense, immence) jungle and across (inpassable, impassable, impassible, inpassible) mountains.

(3) From his (illegible, ilegible, illegable) writing the boy seems to be virtually (iliterate, illiterate, illitterate).

(4) Her (inpudense, impudence, impudense) and (impertinence, inpertinense, inpertinence) are merely signs of her (imaturity, immaturity).

(5) (Irespecrive, irrespective) of its (immediate, imediate) advantages, this proposal is both (inprecise, impresise, imprecise) and (irational, irrational).

(6) I (emplore, implore) you not to (imbark, embark) (impashently, inpatiently, impatiently) upon such an (imperfect, inperfect) plan.

(7) (Imperceptibly, inperseptibly, imperseptibly) the faint (ilumination, illumination) spread throughout the cavern.
(20)

(c) There are mistakes in the following sentences due to the misuse of some of the prefixes we have been looking at. Your job is to put things right.

(1) Misfortunately I undirected him to the non-correct house.

(2) He is disabled to walk because of his unability.

(3) I am taking out an ensurance policy to insure that my family is provided for.

(4) I was very misillusioned when he said it was disbelievable.

(5) I sealed my latest work of fiction in its envelop.
(10)

(d) Here are ten pairs of words that have very similar meanings. (You might like to know that some of them are words with their origins in Latin, while others have come to us from Old English.) Your task is to make the words into their opposites by giving them the correct prefix. (If you are interested, you might like to notice which prefix tends to go with the Latin origin words, and which with the English ones.)

| believable | accessible | precise | sensible | lawful |
| credible | approachable | accurate | conscious | legal |
| licit | mobile | behaviour | logical | conformity |
| proper | movable | subordination | reasonable | orthodoxy (10) |

## SPELLING TESTS

| 1 | 2 | 3 | 4 | 5 |
|---|---|---|---|---|
| unwell | undo | inhuman | encourage | impression |
| immediate | undue | mishap | immature | illustrious |
| impassable | immortal | impertinent | indifferent | unconscious |
| impossible | invisible | mischievous | immunization | impartial |
| unacceptable | enrol | illusion | inconsiderate | inflammable |
| inappropriate | illiterate | impatient | uninhabited | irritation |
| irrigate | invariable | inevitable | illustration | institution |
| unimpressive | uncertain | irresponsible | infuriate | unemployment |
| enthusiasm | independence | unimportant | insufficient | indivisible |
| irrational | investigate | uncomfortable | misinformation | inaccessible |

61

As we briefly mentioned in the last Factsheet, there is another *not* prefix — DIS. You will of course need to learn which words begin with DIS rather than UN, IN or MIS. Also be careful of possible confusion with some words that start with D*E*S. In fact these are mostly words that consist of another prefix, DE, attached to words that originally began with an S. As a general rule, though, words that start with DIS can have the DIS removed, and still mean something (*discover — cover; disobey — obey; disarm — arm*). The words starting with DES are far fewer and if you take the DES off you do not get much! (So there is *desert*, but no 'ert'; *desolate*, but no 'olate'; *destroy*, but no 'troy'.)

DE, by the way, sometimes has a negative idea rather like DIS (as in *defect, decrease, decipher, deform*), but not always, and not always obviously.

There are also some DI words, not connected with DIS or DE; these sometimes have the idea of 'two' about them, as in *dilemma* — a problem with two 'horns' or choices. But again this does not always apply to words that begin with the letters DI (such as *different*, or *difficult*).

## WORDLIST

### DIS WORDS — NEGATIVES

| | | | | OTHER DIS WORDS |
|---|---|---|---|---|
| disable | disconnect | dislike | disqualify | discuss |
| disadvantage | discount | dislocate | dispute | display |
| disagree | discourage | dislodge | disregard | distribute |
| disappear | discover | disloyal | disrupt | disciple |
| disappoint | discriminate | dismay | distract | discipline |
| disapprove | disease | dismiss | distress | district |
| disarm | disgrace | disobey | disturb | distant |
| disaster | disguise | disorder | distrust | dispense |
| discharge | disgust | displace | disuse | dismal |
| discolour | dishonest | displease | disclose | |
| discomfort | disintegrate | disprove | disbelieve | dispatch *or* despatch (!) |

### DE WORDS — NEGATIVE SENSE

### OTHER DE WORDS

| | | | | |
|---|---|---|---|---|
| defrost | defeat | debate | devastate | delegate |
| defuse | delay | decay | deduce | delicate |
| defect | deform | deceive | define | delicatessen |
| deface | degrade | deception | definition | deliberate |
| detract | defile | develop | defend | delicious |
| deduct | deflect | decide | defence | delirious |
| deduction | delinquent | decision | definite | deliver |
| decompose | depart | declare | defy | demand |
| deprive | denounce | decorate | defiant | deluge |
| depress | deny | dedicate | defraud | deposit |
| detour | detest | depict | detect | devotion |
| | | derive | delight | devour |

### DES WORDS

| | | | | |
|---|---|---|---|---|
| despise | designate | desolate | design | deserve |
| despair | destroy | desire | destiny | describe |
| desperate | destruction | despondent | destination | description |

### PAIRS OF WORDS

*Notice that you often get pairs of words with different prefixes:—*

descent *and* descend (*going down*):   ascent *and* ascend (*going up*)

detach (attach)        decline (incline)        deplore (implore)        decrease (increase)

deficient *and* deficiency (efficient *and* efficiency)

*Not all these words are opposites of course, and it is sensible to check the exact meanings in your dictionary.*

### DI WORDS

| | | | | |
|---|---|---|---|---|
| dilemma | diplomacy | diploma | dioxide | diphthong |
| divide | direct | difficult | different | digest |
| division | direction | difficulty | difference | digestion |
| diminish | diverse | divulge | diversion | divorce |

# EXERCISES

(a) Give the opposites of these words, formed by adding one of the prefixes on this Factsheet, or Factsheet Thirty. Be careful when adding some of them — as a spelling change may be involved.

| | | | | |
|---|---|---|---|---|
| unite | do | similar | spell | agree |
| perfect | satisfactory | moral | form | literate (5) |

(b) Once again, put the correct negative prefix on these words. This time you need to be careful because they are in pairs — and the two words in a pair do not have the same prefix.

| | | | | |
|---|---|---|---|---|
| fortune | comfort | please | divided | equal |
| fortunate | comfortable | pleasant | divisible | equality (5) |

(c) Put a negative prefix on each of the following words, which *already* start with one of the prefixes (*in, dis* and *de*) that we have been looking at.

| | | | | |
|---|---|---|---|---|
| inform | integrate | impressed | important | incline |
| dispensible | defiled | incentive | defeated | illusion (5) |

(d) To each of the following words you can add *two* possible negative prefixes. Find out in each case what they are, write down the words, and explain what each of them *means*. It may be that the two possible 'opposites' both mean much the same — or they may have rather different meanings.

| | | | | |
|---|---|---|---|---|
| trust | ease | use | ability | interested (10) |

(e) Here you are given a choice of spellings for the following ten words. You have to choose the correct spelling. In each case this means deciding on a *double* or *single* consonant. (The thing to do is think what the word to which the prefix has been added originally began with . . .)

| | | | | |
|---|---|---|---|---|
| unnatural | disolve | disservice | inumerable | mistate |
| unatural | dissolve | diservice | innumerable | misstate |
| uneducated | dissappear | disunited | innactive | misstake |
| unneducated | disappear | dissunited | inactive | mistake (5) |

(f) Choose the correct spellings from the alternatives offered to you.

(1) Surely she does not (diserve, deserve) to be (desqualified, disqualified).

(2) They have (desided, decided, disided, dicided) to get a (divorce, devorce).

(3) We shall need to (descuss, discuss) the new (disigns, designs) later today.

(4) The destinations of the trains are all clearly (desplayed, displayed) on the (departures, dipartures) board.

(5) Her reaction to the (dilemma, delemma) was to (delay, dilay) her decision.

(6) (Despite, dispite) the approach of the enemy army, the general chose to (devide, divide) his own forces.

(7) Kindly have all my purchases (dilivered, delivered) (derect, direct) to my house.

(8) I have no (disire, desire) to (desieve, deceive, diceive, diseave) them.

(9) I (dispair, despair) of any solution to the present (dispute), despute).

(10) The book (describes, discribes) her latest (discoveries, descoveries) in the field of medicine. (20)

# SPELLING TESTS

| 1 | 2 | 3 | 4 | 5 |
|---|---|---|---|---|
| disadvantage | destroy | describe | disguise | dismal |
| despair | disaster | disciple | description | deserve |
| delinquent | diminish | delight | digestion | delicious |
| division | defiant | direction | deposit | difficulty |
| detach | decrease | deficient | descend | decline |
| attach | increase | efficiency | ascend | divert |
| dismiss | dilemma | discolour | difference | design |
| detour | deceive | divorce | destruction | designation |
| diplomacy | deception | diverse | discipline | disuse |
| disqualify | disease | definition | deduction | disgust |

# FACTSHEET THIRTY-TWO                    OTHER PREFIXES

There are many other prefixes that have entered English from Latin (and a few from Greek!). This page deals with a *few* of the words, under the headings of the different prefixes. Where it might help, the original meanings of the prefixes are mentioned. Possible problem words (for example when adding a prefix changes the spelling, as when SUB + *position* becomes *supposition*) are marked with an exclamation mark (!).

The Wordlist starts with three similar prefixes, PER, PRE and PRO; your aim is not to confuse them . . . There is a great deal of difference between *prefect* and *perfect*!

## WORDLIST

### PER

| | | | | | | |
|---|---|---|---|---|---|---|
| permit | perhaps | perform | perfume | persecute | permanent | perspective |
| permission | persist | perverse | perspire | persuade | perpetual | perpendicular |

### PRE (*PRE sometimes means 'before'.*)

| | | | | | | |
|---|---|---|---|---|---|---|
| prevent | present | preliminary | prefix | predict | prepare | prejudice |
| prescribe | previous | prevail | presume | president | preparatory | preface |

### PRO

| | | | | | | |
|---|---|---|---|---|---|---|
| process | proclaim | produce | profit | progress | profound | profession |
| procession | proclamation | production | project | prohibit | promote | professor |
| pronounce | propose | propel | prospect | provoke | provide | province |
| protect | protest | propeller | prospectus | prominent | programme *or* program | |

### CON (*CON is a very common prefix, that originally meant 'together' or 'with'.*)

| | | | | | | |
|---|---|---|---|---|---|---|
| conceal | conceit | conceive | concern | concert | concentrate | condition |
| conduct | confer | conception | confuse | conscious (!) | conquer | congress |
| concrete | conference | concept | conserve | connect | consonant | consequent |
| construct | consume | convince | continent | contain | contrast | contract |
| contour | convenient | convict | convert | convenient | conspiracy | convey |
| constant | consult | conviction | convent | continue | contaminate | contagious (!) |

### CON in COMBINATIONS (COMB . . . COMP . . . COMM . . . COLL . . . CORR . . .)

| | | | | | | |
|---|---|---|---|---|---|---|
| combine | combustion | combination | (*Notice:* comfort (M *not* N) *and* comrade (MR).) | | | |
| compact | companion | company | compare | compel | compete | complete |
| complain | compile | compose | comparison | compulsion | competition | completion |
| compress | comprise | compromise | compulsory | computer | composition | comprehension |
| command | commence | commerce | commit | commotion | communion | commuter |
| commandment | comment | commercial | committee | communicate | community | commemorate |
| collapse | colleague | collect | college | collide | collaborate | |
| correct | correspond | correspondence corrode | | corrugated | corrupt | |

### EX (*EX originally meant 'out of' — the opposite of IN — and is very common.*)

| | | | | | | |
|---|---|---|---|---|---|---|
| exaggerate | exceed | excellent | excess | excitement | exhaust | exist |
| expedition | exercise (*fitness*) | exorcise (*ghosts*) | | exile | exquisite | extinguish |
| exception | exploit | expensive (*not EXS-!*) | | exterior | (*Beware of:* escape — S *not* X.) | |

### RE (*RE often means 'back' or 'again' — and is even more common.*)

| | | | | | | |
|---|---|---|---|---|---|---|
| rebel | recede | receipt | recite | refill | refer | refrigerate |
| rebellion | recession | reception | recital | renew | referred | refrigerator |
| research | request | reproach | remain | rely | reference | rejoice |
| remedial | reprieve | reservoir | remnant | reliable | relief | recruit |

### SUB (*under*)  submit   suburb   substance   subject   subsidy   subsistence
(*Notice:—* supplement, support, suppose; *these are also words formed by the prefix SUB.*)

### SUPER (*over*)  supervise   supersonic   supermarket   supernatural

### AB  abbreviate (*double B*)   abolish   abstract   abuse   absolute   absent   abhor

### OB  object   oblige   obligation   obscene   obstacle   obsession
(*Notice:—* occult, offend, oppose, opposite *and* oppress — *all also formed from OB!*)

### TRANS (*across*)   transform   translate   transfer   transmission   transparent

### POST (*after*)   postpone   postscript (*what 'P.S.' means*)   post-mortem

### ANTI *and* CONTRA (*against*)   antidote   antifreeze   antiseptic   antibiotics
contradict   contrary   contrast   controversy (O!)

### INTER (*between*)   interfere   intermediate   international   interview   introduce (O!)

## EXERCISES

a) Some of the words in the following sentences have their prefixes omitted. In each case you have to fill in the missing three letters. You only have PER, PRO and PRE to choose from!

    (1)    If you …sist in this …verse attitude you will inevitably …voke a …judicial reaction.

    (2)    The full …spectus outlining the new …posals has been …sented to the …sident of the corporation for his …usal.

    (3)    It is essential to …serve the …portions of the building in the …spectives of the …pendicular lines and faces.

    (4)    In the vice-chancellor's …cession, each …fessor should …cede the members of his faculty.

    (5)    I …sume that the witnesses will be …vided with …manent …tection before the trial.    (10)

b) In the following list of twenty words formed with prefixes, ten are spelt incorrectly. Make a list of the correct words, and a second list of the incorrect ones — together with how they *should* be spelt.

| | | | | |
|---|---|---|---|---|
| subport | comparison | offend | conbine | rely |
| combustion | confront | confort | obpress | commotion |
| conpulsory | comittee | correct | conmunicate | post-mortem |
| suppose | abreviate | conrespondence | objection | exspensive  (10) |

c) Here is another piece from the story of an American at an English school. As you will see, he is still complaining . . . He has also, as usual, spelt some words incorrectly. There are twenty of them — all involving words with the prefixes we have looked at on this Factsheet. Rewrite the passage, correcting the mistakes, and underlining your corrections. (Not all the errors are to do with the prefixes themselves.)

> My first night in that dormitory, I sure wished I had brought along some antefreeze. It was like going to sleep in a refridgerator. This colege may be famous, but no way is it famous for its confort. I reckon the enterior was colder than the extirior. You see the glass in those windows is of the expecially tranceparant kind — there isn't any. So that wind howls through there at suprasonic speed. That would have been enough by itself to pervent anyone getting some sleep — apart from the supernatral. The other students were very eager to tell me all about their resident ghost. They confidently perdicted that he was sure to put on a proformance tonight to comemorate the arrival of an uncouth foreigner in his halls. I was all for staying up to exercise him, but they convinsed me it was too dangerous. I guess they were exagerating, but I didn't want to controdict anyone, since it was their ancestor reppearing out of his gruesome grave. He must have found our bedroom quite cool by conparison.    (20)

d) Here are four groups each of five words. The words in each group have the same ending, but start with different prefixes. Write out the words; next to each word write its particular prefix; and then write its *meaning*. Try to see how the prefixes and meanings fit together.

permit  commit  remit  submit  emit        introduce  reduce  induce  deduce  produce

suppose  impose  oppose  dispose  repose        project  subject  object  reject  deject    (10)

## SPELLING TESTS

| 1 | 2 | 3 | 4 | 5 |
|---|---|---|---|---|
| computer | pronounce | concert | congress | excess |
| previous | perverse | province | perpetual | comprise |
| permission | prevention | prejudice | present | compromise |
| profession | conceit | persuade | president | prevail |
| conceal | committee | controversial | propel | perpendicular |
| colleague | correspondence | relief | propeller | convenient |
| submission | objection | referred | concentrate | supervision |
| exaggerate | excellent | reference | transfer | oppress |
| interview | contradict | transmission | supplement | occult |
| introduce | controversy | obstacle | obligation | antibiotics |

Not all prefixes in English have arrived from foreign languages. Many are plain English and their meanings are therefore usually much more clear. These are words like BE, TO, UP, OVER, UNDER — and many others. The first Wordlist contains some of them — and you should find them less of a problem than the words in the last Factsheet!

## WORDLIST (1)

| BE | UP | OVER | UNDER | OUT | FOR (not 'fore') |
|---|---|---|---|---|---|
| become | uphill | overall | undergo | outbreak | forgive |
| because | uphold | overalls | underfoot | outburst | forbid |
| before | upheaval | overboard | underground | outcast | forlorn |
| begone | upholster | overcoat | undergrowth | outcome | forward |
| below | upkeep | overcome | underline | outdoors | forever (!) |
| behead | uprising | overdone | undermine | outfit | forget |
| belong | upright | overflow | underneath | outing | forsake |
| beside | uproar | overgrown | understand | outlaw | |
| begin | upset | overhear | undertake | outline | FORE (= before) |
| behind | upstairs | overlap | undertaker | outpost | forecast |
| between | upwards | overnight | underwater | outnumber | forehead |
| beneath | | overpower | underclothes | outright | foreman |
| beyond | DOWN | overtake | underpants | outset | foretell |
| betray | downfall | overthrow | | outside | forefathers |
| beware | downhill | overtime | BY | outsider | foreground |
| behave | downstream | overwhelm | by-law/bye-law | outskirts | foremost |
| behalf | downward(s) | overwork | by-election | outspoken | foresee |
| besiege | | oversight | bystander | outstanding | foresight |
| befriend | TO | overseas | by-product | outwards | |
| bewilder | today | | bypass | | WITH |
| bewitch | tonight | WELL | | | within |
| bequeath | tomorrow | well-known | *Note that BI (from the Greek)* | | without |
| bemoan | together | well-being | *means 'two':—* | | withhold |
| befit | toward(s) | *but:—* | binoculars | biplane | withstand |
| belabour | *Not a real* | welfare | bicycle | bisect | withdraw |
| | *'to' word is:* | welcome | binary | bilingual | |
| | toboggan | | | | |

## A AND AD WORDS

The second section on this page concerns words that *start* with A. Some of these have an English prefix, A-, like *ablaze, aboard, alight*; and some begin with AL, like *although* and *always*. (Notice that it is one L, not two.)

You will also find many AD words (like *adverb* and *adapt*) which in fact come from a Latin prefix.

Finally, some problem A words with double consonants have also been included.

## WORDLIST (2)

| A PREFIXES | | AD PREFIXES | A WORDS WITH DOUBLE CONSONANTS | | |
|---|---|---|---|---|---|
| aboard | away | address (!DD) | accomplish | ammunition | arrest |
| abroad | ablaze | admonish | accord | annex (*verb*) | arrange |
| adrift | ashore | addict | account | annexe (*noun*) | arrive |
| afloat | awake | adventure | accurate | annihilate | assembly |
| aloud | asleep | admire | accuse | anniversary | assault |
| across | avoid | adopt | accustom | announce | assent |
| along | avenge | adapt | afford | annoy | assume |
| alive | anew | adjust | affair | annual | assist |
| alike | askew | adore | affect | approach | assess |
| amaze | atone | adverb | aggravate | apply | asset |
| amass | arouse | adjective | aggression | application | assistant |
| afraid | arise | administer | allergy | appoint | associate |
| around | among | administration | alliance | applaud | assure |
| alone | against | adequate | ally | appear | attempt |
| | | adjacent | allege | appeal | attract |
| AL WORDS | | addition | allow | appreciate | attend |
| although | always | adhesive | allay | apprentice | attack |
| almost | already | adversity | | approve | attitude |
| also | altogether | admit | | | |

*You may also come across yet another prefix meaning 'not':— the Greek AN, as in* anaesthetic   anarchy   anaemia.

# WORKSHEET THIRTY-THREE

## EXERCISES

a)  (i)  In the following sentences you will find twenty words with prefixes, which have been mis-spelt. Write out the sentences, putting the errors right. Underline the words you have corrected. (10)

(ii)  There are also ten other words with prefixes. As a piece of revision, make a list of these, and next to each write the prefix it begins with, and the meaning of the word. (10)

(1)  My concern for public wellfare is wellknown.

(2)  The latest forcast predicts a close result in the bye-election.

(3)  I shall never foregive the man who has outwited me.

(4)  You are not permitted to ride a bycycle on the bipass.

(5)  The forman will not wellcome the new restrictions on ovretime.

(6)  All pupils are forebidden to go owtside in the rain.

(7)  Toenight we shall encircle the outposte, and tomorow we shall disperse the garrison and overpour the fortress.

(8)  Our fourfathers bekweathed us a rich inheritance; are we now to beatray the exploits of our predecessors?

b)  (i)  In each of the following sentences there are two words where you have to choose between a single letter spelling, and a double letter spelling. Underline the words you choose when you write out the sentences. (10)

(ii)  In each sentence there is also one word with a prefix. Make a list of these, with their prefixes and meanings — as you did in part (ii) of the first exercise. (10)

(1)  Can you (acount, account) for the disturbance in the grounds of the (academy, accademy) last night, Miss Fortescue?

(2)  The (attoms, atoms) will be (attracted, atracted) to the positive terminal and repelled by the negative.

(3)  By what process did you (arrive, arive) at this (ammount, amount)?

(4)  This (afair, affair) has caused the Board (aggonies, agonies) of indecision.

(5)  The (aggent, agent) has made all the necessary (arrangements, arangements) for the removal.

(6)  We have received an (anouncement, announcement) that there is to be a general (alert, allert).

(7)  I (asure, assure) you that there is no need to become (allarmed, alarmed).

(8)  (Asembly, assembly) today will have to be held in the (annexe, anexe).

(9)  The (apprentice, aprentice) (apologized, appologized) to his master for the mistake.

(10)  Miss Taken (allways, always) (alows, allows) us to use the dictionary for translations.

c)  In this exercise you are given a group of words, each of which can have two prefixes added*. In each case the prefixes are those included in the first Wordlist, but *not* all the words you are trying to make are included. Write out each word, and the two words you have formed from it.

| hill | pass | take | line | stand |
| go | come | side | right | sight | (10) |

*Award yourself a bonus mark if you found three for any of them!

## SPELLING TESTS

| 1 | 2 | 3 | 4 | 5 |
|---|---|---|---|---|
| aboard | amass | forever | forehead | forbid |
| abroad | amaze | tomorrow | forsake | foretell |
| besiege | address | avoid | always | addict |
| arouse | admit | apply | annual | underground |
| overwhelm | well-being | although | welcome | atonement |
| already | welfare | upheaval | adore | agreement |
| adopt | alliance | adequate | annoy | aggression |
| afford | bicycle | assess | adjective | altogether |
| binoculars | anniversary | addition | apprentice | assistant |
| appreciate | ammunition | by-election | administration | adhesive |

67

This page largely consists of words which have caused people problems. We have already dealt with some of them, but they are well worth revising. Others will be new to you. Do continue to keep your own list of those *you* find difficult.

The words are grouped together, and where necessary a note is made of the particular problem in the spelling that you must watch out for.

## WORDLIST

### SILENT LETTERS

| | | | | | | | |
|---|---|---|---|---|---|---|---|
| hymn | (MN) | chimney | (*no* L) | parliament | (IA) | subtle | (B) |
| column | (MN) | | | government | (N) | | |
| condemn | (MN) | answer | (W) | indictment | (C) | mistletoe | (TLE) |
| solemn | (MN) | Wednesday | (!) | | | christen | (CH *and silent* T) |

### IE and EI

| | | | | | | | | | |
|---|---|---|---|---|---|---|---|---|---|
| fiend | friend | fiery | grief | mischief | siege | yield | relief | thieves | society |
| weird | freight | forfeit | counterfeit | seize | ceiling | receipt | foreign | eighth | |

### DOUBLE CONSONANTS

| | | | | | | |
|---|---|---|---|---|---|---|
| abbreviate | accommodate | addition | address | appal | assassinate | battalion |
| commemorate | committee | disappoint | embarrass | exaggerate | innocence | immense |
| occupy | occasion | opponent | parallel | paraffin | possess | quarrel |
| rotten | stubbornness | suddenness | tobacco | tyranny | woollen | vaccinate |
| inflammable | difficulty | withhold | | | | |

### SINGLE CONSONANTS

| | | | | | |
|---|---|---|---|---|---|
| balance | Britain | mackerel | derelict | prison | relative | stony (*no* E) |

### TROUBLESOME LETTER C

| | | | | | | |
|---|---|---|---|---|---|---|
| sacrifice | prejudice | procedure | atrocity | exercise | magnificent | incident |
| pronunciation | fascinate (SC) | necessarily (C, *then* SS) | | success (CC *then* SS) | | census |
| accident (CC) | schedule (SCH) | precede (*go first*) | proceed (*go on*) | ancient | | |

### TROUBLESOME ENDINGS

beginning (NN)      inferred (RR) *but* inference (R)      preferred (RR) *but* preference (R)
omit (T) *and* omitted (TT)      limit (T) *and* limited (*also* T)
*Remember the rule about STRESS!*
propel *but* propeller (ER)      buried *but* hurried      coming      developed

### OUS

conscientious (!)      curious *but* curiosity      vicious (!)      miscellaneous (LL *and an* E)
anxious *and* anxiety      conscious (SC)      humour *but* humorous      disastrous (*not* ER)
impetuous *and* tempestuous (U + OUS)      mysterious      courageous (E)

### IA

| | | | | | | | |
|---|---|---|---|---|---|---|---|
| diamond | diary | giant | carriage | familiar | initiative | beneficial | substantial |

### UA *and* AU

| | | | | | | | | |
|---|---|---|---|---|---|---|---|---|
| guard | guarantee | persuade | casualty | *but*:— gauge | gauze | | restaurant | cause |

### ER, AR *and* OR — *and some similar problems*

| | | | | | |
|---|---|---|---|---|---|
| visitor | squalor | governor | impostor | *Also notice*:— | grandeur | chauffeur |
| similar | grammar | collar | calendar | | creature | feature |
| honour | colour | behaviour | | | murmur | volunteer |
| imaginary | boundary | temporary (ARY) | laboratory (ORY) | confectionery (ERY) | | |

### ABLE *and* IBLE

| | | | | |
|---|---|---|---|---|
| irreparable | *Notice the E in*:— changeable | noticeable | peaceable | serviceable |
| incredible | irresistible | responsible | audible | accessible |

*Last but not least difficult — some words from the* GREEK

| | | | | | | |
|---|---|---|---|---|---|---|
| rhubarb | rheumatism | rhododendron | catarrh | paralysis | glycerine | chrysanthemum |
| psychology | psychiatrist | geography | geometry | archaeology | autobiography | zoology |
| microscope | telescope | philosophy | philately | monopoly | monotony | monologue |
| labyrinth | synonym | catastrophe | apostrophe | metamorphosis | encyclopaedia | xenophobia |

## EXERCISES

(a) This is one of the exercises where you have to select the correct spelling from the choices provided in the brackets. Not all the words, or the particular forms of the words, are in the Factsheet, so check with your dictionary.

    (1) Everyone will (condemn, condenm) the (mischeif, mischief) done on this (ocasion, occasion, ocassion, occassion).

    (2) Following the Prime Minister's (anwser, answer) the (goverment, government) (suffered, sufferred) a (disasterous, disastrous) defeat in the (parlimentary, parliamentary) debate.

    (3) The robbers (quarreled, quarrelled) over the division of the (daimonds, diamonds), and there, in the (squalor, squaler) of a (derelict, derrelict) building, their sudden (imense, immense) wealth brought them only (greif, grief).

    (4) Elizabeth's (impetous, impetuous) (behaviour, behavior) (embarrassed, embarased, embraced, embarassed) everyone on the (commitee, committee).

    (5) The (unparaleled, unparalleled) (suddeness, suddenness) of her resignation (nesessarily, necessarily) (cuased, caused) considerable (difficulties, dificulties).

    (6) Work will (proceed, precede) on the temporary (laboratory, laboratry) (acording, according) to (shcedule, schedule).

    (7) The (inflamable, inflammable) properties of the (parafin, parrafin, paraffin) (gauranteed, guarranteed, guaranteed) a (fiery, feiry) end to the (mysterous, mysterious) (creacher, creature).

    (8) I find that a spoonful of (glyserine, glycerine) often eases my (catarhr, catarrh).

    (9) Lost in the (labirinth, labyrinth) of my (goemetry, geometry) homework, my mind was abruptly (seized, siezed) by an (iresistable, irresistable, irresistible, iresistible) (paralysis, paralisis). (20)

(b) To each of the following words add the ending you are given. Consider carefully whether you need to make any other changes when you do so!

| begin (ING) | refer (ED) | refer (ENCE) | hurry (ED) | bury (ING) |
|---|---|---|---|---|
| propel (ER) | travel (ING) | shelter (ED) | come (ING) | panic (ED) (!) (5) |

(c) In this exercise you also have to add the endings you are given to the list of words. Once again be careful of other changes that must be made.

| mystery (OUS) | humour (OUS) | tempest (OUS) | miscellany (OUS) | grief (OUS) |
|---|---|---|---|---|
| carry (AGE) | wool (EN) | prejudice (AL) | necessary (LY) | stubborn (NESS) (5) |

(d) Here is an extract from a story about an adventure in a lost city. The heroine seems to be a female version of Indiana Jones — only tougher. But she never could spell properly. Write out the passage again correcting the *forty* spelling mistakes in it.

Christine puased in the shadow of a great colunm coverred with wierd carvings that comemorated the victories of some anceint and forgoten ruler. Annother time she might have ben fassinated by them, and by the grandour of the lost city. Today her onely thort was excape. For in her hand, rapped in roten parchment, lay the object for which she had sacrifised so much. Other arceologists had scorned her beleif in its very existence. Her adresses to learned sosieties had been recieved first with embarasment and later with luaghter. The neccessary funds had been witheld from her through the prejudise of her former coleags. Her freinds had tried to persaude her to abandon the search for this imajinery thing, but she had continued tenashusly in her great quest. Now, finaly, she knew she had been right. For what she held was the fabullous filosofers' stone — lost for a thousand years in the catastrophy that had cast down the ruined city around her. By its power could be accomplished the metamorphosice from one state to another:— lead into gold, perhaps even death into life. — An angry murmure of voices in the distance called her back to realty. The gaurdians of the secret would not give it up to her so easily. (20)

## SPELLING TESTS

| 1 | 2 | 3 | 4 | 5 |
|---|---|---|---|---|
| chimney | parliament | mistletoe | fiend | Wednesday |
| eighth | occupation | occasion | weird | tyranny |
| society | difficulty | possession | withhold | vaccination |
| receipt | mackerel | imprisonment | atrocity | accidentally |
| propeller | fascinate | schedule | preferred | humour |
| consciousness | courageous | beneficial | preference | humorous |
| diamond | guarantee | restaurant | squalor | laboratory |
| casualty | temporary | miscellaneous | behaviour | creature |
| changeable | telescope | apostrophe | monologue | initiative |
| rhubarb | synonym | rheumatism | psychiatrist | encyclopaedia |

# REVISION EXERCISES

These are exercises for when you have finished the book — to see how good your spelling is!

(a)  These sentences were written by a small child who has not read the book. He spells many words rather 'interestingly'
See if you can put things right.

    (1)  I woz stung by a wosp; it geiv me sutch a shok.

    (2)  Wear where my frends wen I kneaded them?

    (3)  I get an ake in my hart as my thorts tern to ewe.

    (4)  I sore the buoy get into yore bote and pick up the ores.

    (5)  Theirs no dout its my towl, you theif!

(30)

(b)  Here you are given two or more meanings that each refer to a pair or group of homophones. (E.g. *past tense of*
*eat* and *number after seven = ate* and *eight* — in that order.)
Insert the correct words, correctly spelt, with the following meanings:—

| (1) | – king's seat<br>– hurled | (3) | – appear to be<br>– sewn join | (6) | – sea's edge<br>– quite certain | (9) | – correct<br>– religious ceremony |
|---|---|---|---|---|---|---|---|
| (2) | – precious stone<br>– with two parts<br>– fight between<br>  two people | (4) | – female horse<br>– town chief | (7) | – one who foresees<br>– a gain/to gain | | – to use a pen<br>– a craftsman |
| | | (5) | – permitted<br>– not silent | (8) | – to decrease<br>– a teaching session | (10) | – a dried fruit<br>– flow of water or<br>  electricity |

(30)

(c)  Make the following plural:—

    thief   monkey   salmon   terminus   search   activity   loss   plateau   policewoman   mother-in-law (10)

(d)  Put the following verbs into the past tense:—

    scatter   refer   travel   market   admit   light   lie   fly   wind   beat (10)

(e)  Make the following into nouns ending in ION:—

    suspicious   act   inform   unite   compose   retain   permit   educate   include   add (10)

(f)  Make words ending in OUS out of the following:—

    tempest   anxiety   grace   jealousy   victory   curiosity   generosity   marvel   courage (10)

(g)  Make words ending in TY out of the following:—

    honest   possible   liable   gay   infinite   safe   pious   various   simple   necessary (10)

(h)  Add the correct ending from AL, EL and LE to each of the following:—

    cast..   spani..   loy..   ax..   leg..   eag..   tri..   pan..   padd..   ting.. (10)

(i)  Add the correct ending from AR, ER, OR and RE to each of the following:—

    debt..   li..   ward..   cell..   cent..   schol..   high..   burgl..   warri..   engine.. (10)

(j)  Make the following words into negative abstract nouns (!) — by adding a negative prefix, and a noun ending. (So
'familiar' would produce '*un*familiar*ity*'.)

    agree   happy   employ   secure   please   suitable   mobile   able   responsible   proper (20)

(k)  We can't finish without a last visit to the 'Yank' at school . . .

    They have this quiant ritaul here called 'Lights Out'. The thoery is that there has to be total silense — not just reguler quite. We wernt even aloud to talk. — Of coars I did not think you were ment to take this sereously. So when some kid calling himself a perfect came into the dormitry, I gess I was haveing a conversasion. Well, I maintained that I was not speaking allowed; in fact my vioce was no more than a wisper. But this trecherus leiutenant of the Brittish tyrrany that opressed us poor students greated my protestions with luahgter and dirision. Even my felow suferors showed no simpathy with my plite. I was comanded to stand to atension in the icey coridor, untill the principle himself could deal with me.

    "Say, you gies did abollish corprol punishment?" I asked as I left.

    "That is the leste of your wories," came the anser — from a suposed friend.

    As I stood there, shivering in the cold, their came to my ears the faint sound of chains rattling and clanking in the distence. I rememberred with horrer that tonight the ghost was dew to walk. I ask you, is this what my pa was paying fifty bucks an hour for? (50)

He can't spell . . . but he has a good vocabulary! — You should have found *fifty* mistakes!

There are four sets of tests on this page; the first three cover particular Factsheets, and the final one is more general — and harder!

(a)  *Tests based on Factsheets One to Thirteen*

| 1 | 2 | 3 | 4 | 5 |
|---|---|---|---|---|
| break | wreck | wrap | friend | reign |
| dealt | siege | gauge | dear | rain |
| knelt | prayer | ease | deer | rein |
| limb | thought | lymph | sieve | wrist |
| guide | weave | choir | wasp | child |
| though | night | ghost | wrong | dawn |
| sluice | knight | known | view | sword |
| bough | force | noun | took | fraud |
| bow | horse | could | school | move |
| urge | pearl | thumb | chasm | thirst |

(b)  *Tests based on Factsheets Fourteen to Twenty-Two*

| 1 | 2 | 3 | 4 | 5 |
|---|---|---|---|---|
| habit | antique | focus | crisis | monarch |
| referred | prison | pity | travelling | appeal |
| reference | admit | flattened | heroes | swallow |
| gases | admitted | copy | arisen | tiny |
| its | dealt | pianos | occur | thieves |
| it's | associate | taught | acquaint | swollen |
| discipline | margarine | scheme | wreckage | ocean |
| February | leisure | conceive | lightning | valuable |
| accent | symphony | ceiling | scientific | haulage |
| ascent | government | sealing | marriage | skeleton |

(c)  *Tests based on Factsheets Twenty-Three to Thirty-Four*

| 1 | 2 | 3 | 4 | 5 |
|---|---|---|---|---|
| terminal | regimental | fulfil | agriculture | message |
| cancel | accession | juvenile | appreciation | occupation |
| vehicle | affectionate | alcohol | resolution | commission |
| suspicion | agility | sovereignty | reliability | ceremony |
| vacancy | identification | lawyer | tragedy | emperor |
| seriously | auctioneer | authorization | machinery | malicious |
| illusion | disobedience | efficiency | immunize | accidentally |
| corrugated | awfulness | institution | definition | illustrious |
| persuasion | precede | contagion | appreciate | attitude |
| scholarship | proceed | familiarity | noticeable | restaurant |

(d)  *General Tests of more difficult words*

| 1 | 2 | 3 | 4 | 5 |
|---|---|---|---|---|
| twelfth | precious | headache | deterrent | paraphrase |
| phlegm | endeavour | priesthood | roguish | psychological |
| sphinx | juiciness | crucial | solicitor | tautology |
| schism | society | provocation | mechanically | schematic |
| myrrh | anniversaries | allegedly | certificate | synonymous |
| daughter | acquaintance | concerto | confederacy | crystalline |
| disease | advertisement | possession | changeable | pneumonia |
| deceive | civilization | insufficiency | accomplishment | metamorphosis |
| commotion | entombment | controversial | symmetry | rhinoceroses |
| proficiency | disciplinarian | Christianity | fluorescent | autobiographically |

There is of course a vast number of words in the English language, and only a selection have been included in this book. Many of the words not included can be spelt correctly using the rules, principles and advice given to you. Others you will need to learn specially. It is sensible to continue to keep your own spelling notebook, with your particular problem words in — and in which you can write new words to learn as you come across them. Remember to keep a note of meanings (when you do not know them) as well as spellings — and try to use new words in the correct way, and correctly spelt, in your own writing.

The words in the rest of this book have largely been grouped together by *sound*. This list, however, is in alphabetical order, to help you look up some of the more difficult words. It is not a complete list (that would need another book). Nor is it a dictionary: meanings of words have only been included where they are needed to avoid confusion. What it is intended to do is to give a summary of words which people have often found hard to spell, particularly longer and more complicated words.

| ABI to ALL | ALL to AQU | ARC to AWK | BAC to CAM |
|---|---|---|---|
| ability | allowed (*permitted*) | architecture | bachelor |
| accelerator | aloud (*not silent*) | Arctic | bacteria |
| accent (*speech*) | already | argue | ballet |
| accept(*take*) | altar (*church*) | argument | barbecue |
| access | alter (*change*) | arise | barometer |
| accident | although | aristocracy | barrier |
| accommodation | aluminium | armour | basically |
| accompany | amateur | artificial | beautiful |
| accuracy | ambassador | ascend (*go up*) | beauty |
| accuse | ambitious | ascent (*going up*) | behaviour |
| ache | ammunition | aspirin | belief (*noun*) |
| achieve | anaesthetic | assassinate | believe (*verb*) |
| acid | analyse | assault | bellow (*shout*) |
| acquaint | ancestor | assembly | below (*underneath*) |
| acquit | anchor | assess | benefit |
| actually | ancient | assist | benefited |
| address | anniversary | association | bicycle |
| adhesive | announcement | assurance | binoculars |
| admission | annual | astronaut | biology |
| admittance | anonymous | asylum | bouquet |
| advice (*noun*) | answer | atmosphere | bridal (*of a bride*) |
| advise(*verb*) | Antarctic | atrocious | bridle (*harness*) |
| aerial | antenna | attachment | brief |
| aeroplane | antique | attitude | brilliant |
| aerosol | antiseptic | attractive | bruise |
| affect (*verb*) | anxiety | auction | brunette |
| agency | anxious | audible | buoy (*in the sea*) |
| aggravate | apology | audience | bureau |
| aggressive | apparatus | audition | bureaux |
| agile | apparent | author | burglar |
| agony | applause | autobiography | calculator |
| agricultural | appliance | autumn | calendar |
| aisle (*in church*) | appreciation | auxiliary | camera |
| alcohol | appropriate | available | camouflage |
| allergy | aquarium | awkward | campaign |

## CAN to CHE

cancel
cancer
capacity
carriage
cashier
casserole
cassette
casualty
catalogue
catarrh
catastrophe
cathedral
caught (*to catch*)
cauliflower
cause
cautious
cease
ceiling (*roof*)
celebrate
cell (*prison*)
cellar (*basement*)
cement
centimetre
centre
century
cereal (*grain*)
ceremony
certificate
chalet
challenge
champagne
changeable
channel
chaos
chaotic
character
chassis
chauffeur
chef
chemical
cheque (*money*)

## CHI to COM

chief
chimney
choir
chorus
christening
Christian
Christmas
chrome
chronic
chrysalis
cigarette
circle
circular
circumference
citizen
city
civilian
classification
coarse (*rough*)
coax
cocoa
coconut
coincidence
collage (*art*)
collapsible
colleague
collector
college (*university*)
collision
colossal
colour
column
combed
comedian
comfortable
commentator
commit
committee
commotion
community
companion

## COM to CORR

compass
compel
competition
completion
complexion
compliment (*praise*)
comprehension
comprehensive
compression
compulsory
computer
conceal
concentration
concern
concert
concussion
condemn
confectionery
confess
confetti
confidential
confiscate
congratulations
conjuror
conscience
conscientious
conscious
consequence
conspicuous
constellation
consumption
continual
continuous
contractor
convenient
co-operate
coronation
correction
correspondence
corridor
corrugated

## COU to DEC

cough
could
council
councillor (*elected*)
counsellor (*adviser*)
counterfeit
coupon
courage
course (*track*)
court (*law*)
courteous
courtesy
cousin
cowardice
create
creator
creature
criminal
crisis
criticism
crockery
crocodile
cruelty
crystal
cucumber
cupboard
curiosity
curious
currant (*fruit*)
current (*flow*)
cushion
cycling
cylinder
daffodil
dairy (*milk*)
dandelion
dangerous
daughter
debt
deceitful
decent (*proper*)

| DEC to DIA | DIA to EDI | EFF to EXC | EXH to FUR |
|---|---|---|---|
| decision | diameter | effect (*noun*) | exhaust |
| decimal | diamond | efficiency | exhibition |
| deduce (*work out*) | diarrhoea | eight | existence |
| deduct (*subtract*) | diary (*book*) | eighth | expel |
| defence | dictionary | either | expensive |
| defensive | diesel | electrician | experience |
| defiance | diet | electricity | expulsion |
| definitely | difference | embarrass | exterior |
| defy | difficulty | embassy | extinguisher |
| delicacy | digestion | embroidery | extraordinary |
| delicious | dignified | emerald | fabulous |
| delight | dilapidated | emigrate (*go out*) | familiar |
| delinquency | dinosaur | emotional | famous |
| democracy | director | emphasis (*noun*) | farther (*distant*) |
| demolition | discipline | emphasize (*verb*) | fascinate |
| demonstrator | disconnect | encyclopaedia | fashionable |
| depot | discuss (*talk about*) | energetically | faulty |
| depth | disease | energy | ferocious |
| derelict | disguise | engineer | ferocity |
| descend (*go down*) | disgust (*loathing*) | enough | feud |
| descent (*going down*) | dishonest | enquiry (*or* inquiry) | fibre |
| descendant | disobedience | enthusiasm | fictitious |
| description | dispatch (*or* despatch) | entirely | field |
| desert | disposal | envelope (*noun*) | fierce |
| design | disqualified | envious | fiery |
| despair | dissolve | epidemic | financial |
| despatch (*or* dispatch) | distinguished | equality | flavour |
| desperation | diversion | equator | fluent |
| despise | divorce | equipment | fluid |
| dessert (*pudding*) | documentary | eraser | fluorescent |
| destroyer | dormitory | erratic | forecast |
| detention | doubt | error | foreigner |
| detergent | dough | eruption | forfeit |
| detonator | drought | escalator | fragile |
| develop | duel | essay | fraud |
| development | dyeing (*colouring*) | essentially | freight |
| device (*noun*) | dynamite | evacuation | friend |
| devise (*verb*) | easier | exaggeration | frontier |
| diagnosis | eccentric | excellent | furious |
| dial | echoes | except (*leaving out*) | furry (*with fur*) |
| dialogue | edit | excitement | fury (*rage*) |

| GAL to HEA | HEI to INC | IND to JUS | KHA to LYN |
|---|---|---|---|
| galaxy | height | indigestible | khaki |
| gauge | hideous | individual | kilometre |
| gauze | hilarious | inefficient | kiosk |
| generator | hindrance | inflammable | knead (*dough*) |
| generous | holiday | influential | knight |
| generosity | honourable | influenza | knowledge |
| genuine | horrible | infuriate | knuckle |
| geography | horror | ingenious | laboratory |
| ghastly | humorous | ingenuity | labourer |
| ghostly | humour | ingredients | language |
| giant | hurricane | initial | laughter |
| gigantic | hydraulic | initiative | launderette |
| gipsy (*or* gypsy) | hydro-electric | innocence | lawyer |
| glamorous | hydrogen | inoculation | league |
| glamour | hygiene | inquire (*or* enquire) | legacy |
| glorious | hymn | inquisitive | legendary |
| gnaw | hypnotize | install | legible |
| gorgeous | hypocrisy | instalment | legion |
| government | hysterical | insurance | leisurely |
| gracious | ideally | intelligent | lengthen |
| gradual | idiot | interior | lenient |
| grammar | illegal | intermediate | leopard |
| gratefully | illegible | interruption | lessen (*decrease*) |
| grief (*noun*) | illiterate | interview | lesson (*teaching*) |
| grieve (*verb*) | illuminate | introduction | lettuce |
| grocery | illustration | invalid | liable |
| grotesque | imaginary | irregular | liar |
| gruesome | immediate | irresponsible | libel (*like slander*) |
| guess | immigrate (*come into*) | irrigation | librarian |
| guest | immune | irritation | licence (*noun*) |
| guidance | impatience | island | license (*verb*) |
| guilty | impression | issue | lieutenant |
| guitar | inaccurate | its (*of it*) | limited |
| gymnasium | inaudible | it's (*it is*) | listening |
| gypsy (*or* gipsy) | incense | javelin | loathsome |
| handkerchief | incentive | jealousy | logical |
| haphazard | incidental | jewellery | luminous |
| happiness | incompetence | journey | lunar |
| harbour | inconvenience | judging | luscious |
| haunted | incorrect | juicy | luxurious |
| heavier | incredible | justice | lynch |

### MAC to MIS

macaroni
machinery
magician
magnificent
maintain
maintenance
manager
maniac
mannequin
manners
manoeuvre
manor (*house*)
manslaughter
mantelpiece
manual
margarine
margin
martyr
marvel
marvellous
material
mayor
medieval
medicine
memorial
mercury
mercy
messenger
metallic
meteor
meteorology
meter (*that measures*)
metre (*a measurement*)
microphone
midday
mileage
millimetre
millionaire
miniature
miraculous
misbehaviour

### MIS to NOT

mischief
mischievous
missile
mission
molecule
molecular
momentary
monastery
monopoly
monotonous
monstrous
mortgage
mosaic
mosque
mosquito
mouldy
moustache
murderer
murmur
muscle
muscular
museum
musician
mutineer
mutiny
mutual
mysterious
mystery
narrator
national
naughty
necessary
necessity
neighbour
neither
neon
nephew
neutral
niece
noticeable
notorious

### NOU to OPT

nourishment
novelist
nuclear
nucleus
nuisance
nursery
nutrition
nylon
obedient
objectionable
oblige
oblique
obscene
obscenity
obsession
obstinacy
obvious
occasionally
occupation
occur
occurred
occurrence
ocean
odour
offence
offensive
officer
official
omelette
ominous
omission
omit
omitted
onion
opaque
opinion
opponent
opportunity
opposite
optician
option

### ORC to PER

orchestra
origin
originality
orphan
outrageous
overhaul
overwhelm
oxygen
oyster
panic
panicked
parachute
paraffin
paragraph
parallel
parliament
partial
participate
particularly
passenger
pathetic
patient
pause
pavilion
peculiar
pedal (*cycle*)
pedestrian
penalty
penguin
penicillin
pensioner
people
perennial
perilous
perimeter
period
permission
permit
permitted
perpetual
persecution

| PER to POT | PRA to PRO | PRO to REC | REC to SAT |
|---|---|---|---|
| personal (*private*) | practice (*noun*) | proportion | recruit |
| personnel (*people*) | practise (*verb*) | proprietor | refer |
| perspiration | prairie | protein | reference |
| persuade | praise | provincial | referred |
| persuasion | prayer | provision | refrigerator |
| pessimist | precious | psychology | refugee |
| petition | precipice | punctuation | regiment |
| phantom | precise | pursuit | regional |
| pheasant | precision | pyjamas | regrettable |
| phosphorus | prefer | pylon | regular |
| phosphorescent | preference | pyramid | rehearsal |
| photography | preferred | python | reign (*monarch*) |
| phrase | pregnant | qualify | rein (*bridle*) |
| physics | prehistoric | quantity | reinforcements |
| physique | prejudice | quarrelled | reliable |
| pianist | premier | quarry | relief (*noun*) |
| picnic | prestige | quartz | relieve (*verb*) |
| picnicking | presumably | quay (*dock*) | religious |
| pictorial | prettier | query | remedy |
| picturesque | previous | questionnaire | renewal |
| piece | prey (*victim*) | quiet (*silent*) | repetition |
| pier (*jetty*) | principal (*chief*) | quite (*rather*) | reprieve |
| pigeon | principle (*a rule*) | quotation | reservoir |
| pigmy | priority | racial | resin |
| pioneer | privilege | radiator | resourceful |
| plague | proceed | rarity | responsibility |
| plaice (*fish*) | process | raspberry | restaurant |
| plumber | procession | ratio | retaliate |
| pneumatic | prodigy | ration | rheumatism |
| pneumonia | professional | razor | rhinoceros |
| poetry | professor | reality | rhubarb |
| poisonous | profit (*gain*) | rebellion | rhythm |
| policy | projector | receipt | rogue |
| politician | pronounce | reception | rumour |
| pollution | pronunciation | recipe | sabotage |
| polythene | propaganda | recitation | saccharin |
| pompous | propel | reckon | sacrifice |
| porcelain | propeller | recognize | salary |
| porous | prophecy (*noun*) | recommend | sandwich |
| possess | prophesy (*verb*) | reconnaissance | sapphire |
| potential | prophet (*foresees*) | recreation | satchel |

### SAT to SIL

satellite
satisfaction
saucer
saviour
savoury
scarcity
scenery
scent (*smell*)
schedule
scheme
scholarship
school
science
scientifically
scissors
scythe
secondary
secrecy
secretary
seize
semicircle
sensational
sensibly
sequel
sequence
sergeant
serial (*episodes*)
series
serious
serviette
session
settee
severity
sewage
sheik
shepherd
sieve
signature
significant
silence
silhouette

### SIL to STA

silicon
similar
simplicity
simulation
simultaneous
sincerely
sinew
siphon
situation
skeleton
skiing
slaughter
sleuth
smoulder
soar (*fly high*)
social
society
solar
soldier
solemn
solicitor
solitary
soloist
sonic
spacious
spaghetti
special
species
specific
specimen
speech
sphere
sponsor
spontaneous
squabbling
squadron
squirrel
stationary (*still*)
stationery (*paper*)
statistics
statue

### STE to SYS

stewardess
stomach
storey (*of a house*)
straightforward
strength
studio
style
submerge
substantial
succeed
success
suction
sufficient
suffocate
sugar
suggestion
suicide
suit (*clothes*)
suite (*furniture*)
sulphur
summary
summit
superiority
superstitious
supervisor
surgeon
surgery
surprise
surrender
surround
surveyor
survival
suspicious
swollen
sword
syllable
sympathy
synthetic
syringe
syrup
system

### TAN to TRA

tangerine
taught (*teach*)
taut (*tight*)
technical
technique
telephone
temperamental
temperature
temporary
temptation
tension
tentacle
terrible
terrier
territory
terror
testimonial
theatre
their (*of them*)
theory
there (*that place*)
thermometer
thieves
thorough
though
thought
tightness
tobacco
toboggan
toffee
tonsilitis
tortoise
total
tough
tournament
traffic
tragedy
tragic
tranquillizer
transfer
transferred

### TRA to UNN

transistor
translation
transmit
transmitter
treachery
treason
treasury
tremendous
trespasser
triangular
triumph
trophy
trough
truancy
truant
truncheon
tycoon
typewriter
typical
tyre (*rubber*)
ulcer
umbrella
unanimous
unconscious
unnatural
unnecessary

### UNU to VES

unusual
urgent
usually
utensil
utility
utmost
vacancy
vaccination
vacuum
valid
valuable
varied
variety
various
vault
vegetable
vehicle
veil
vein
velocity
vengeance
ventilation
ventriloquist
version
vertical
vessel

### VIC to WHI

vicious
villain
vinegar
violent
violin
virtually
visible
visitor
vocabulary
voucher
vowel
waiter
warrant
wary
wealthy
weapon
weather (*rain*)
weigh
weight
weird
welfare
wellingtons
whereabouts
whirlwind
whisky
whisper

### WHI to ZER

whistling
who's (*who is*)
wholly
whom
whose (*of whom*)
width
woollen
worried
worse (*more bad*)
worst (*most bad*)
would
wrapped
wreath
wreckage
wrench
wrestling
wriggle
wring (*twist*)
wrinkle
wrist
write (*use a pen*)
wrong (*incorrect*)
wrung (*twisted*)
xylophone
yacht
zero

# INDEX

*For revision notes on some problem words, see Page 68.*